W9-DEY-010

Some Gold, a Little Ivory

Some Gold, a Little Ivory

Country Tales from Ghana and the Ivory Coast

Collected, edited and illustrated by Edythe Rance Haskett

The John Day Company   •   *New York*

To my son John
his wife Yvonne and
their son Tony

ALSO BY EDYTHE RANCE HASKETT
Grains of Pepper: Folk Tales from Liberia

The John Day Company, 257 Park Avenue South, New York, N.Y. 10010
an Intext publisher

Published on the same day in Canada by Longmans Canada Limited.

Library of Congress Catalogue Card Number: 70-124154
Printed in the United States of America
Designed by The Etheredges

Contents

Introduction

In the early fifteenth century, Portuguese explorers on their way to the Orient stopped along the west coast of Africa to replenish their food and water supplies. Intrigued by the vastness of a continent that so little was known about, many of the explorers established trading stations in order to barter with the natives, and named these coastal trading stations after the bountiful products found in each locality.

In one area they found pepper growing. This became the Grain Coast (now Liberia and Sierra Leone). These "grains of paradise" were useful in seasoning and preserving food for the explorers' long journeys to the Middle and Far East.

As these adventurous sailors moved on down the coast, they encountered bull elephants with magnificent tusks, and native peoples arrayed in beautiful ivory bangles and beads. In this area they traded their European products for the huge tusks, which they took to India and China. They named this trading area the Ivory Coast, the name it still bears today.

In the adjoining territory, the Portuguese navigators were astounded by the sight of yellow sand that shone like gold in the noonday sun. Gold nuggets were found along the riverbanks. Such riches, obtainable without too much trouble, led to the establishment of permanent trading stations along this bountiful coast. They named this area the Gold Coast and initiated a brisk trading relationship with the natives.

As the years went by, the trading in gold and ivory declined, and another item entered the market. Tribal chiefs who were eager to get rid of their captured enemies offered their most important prisoners to the foreigners in exchange for "magical" firearms. Thus began the trade in "black gold," as the slaves were called, and the area south of Ghana, from the Gulf of Guinea to the Congo, became known as the infamous Slave Coast.

Much has changed in West Africa since that long-ago time. The Gold Coast became an independent nation in 1957, and took the name Ghana from an old Sudanese kingdom that existed around A.D. 700. The Ivory Coast has retained its old name, but prior to 1946 it was a part of French West Africa. Since 1959, it too has gained independence.

Industry, commerce, education, roads, and systems of communication have brought progress to Ghana and the Ivory Coast. But far away from the busy, bustling, heavily populated cities, the up-country tribal people, who live in the small mud hut villages where the roads do not reach, still cling to the customs and traditions of their ancestors.

When the busy workdays are over, and darkness steals across the sky, the storyteller gathers the young and old around him to retell the old, old stories of bygone days. With a variety of voices and gestures, the storyteller spices the night with tales of man-woman "palaver," or the humorous stories of animals who talk and act like people.

Although story time is a time of fun and relaxation, it is then that the young ones are told the history and legends of their people. The fun stories are designed to teach fair play, honesty, sharing, and loyalty.

The old and young alike relish the animal stories that cleverly parallel incidents in their own lives. Besides humor, the stories provide a harmless way to get a message across to a lazy, bothersome, dishonest, wrong-doing chief or neighbor.

The busy noises of the cities are far, far away as the old storyteller begins, "Once upon a time . . ." The audience answers him with a respectful silence. All are at peace. Only the sound of the night "things" and the voice of the story man break the silence. If you sit quietly and turn a page, perhaps you can still hear his voice, as he shares some gold and a little ivory with you.

Mahada and the Bull Elephant

(Ivory Coast)

In the distant village of Ghadiene lived the widow Mahda and her four children. Since the death of her husband two years ago, all the townspeople had helped Mahda with her small farm and the rearing of her children.

Mahda was always strict with her girls and did not allow them to wander far from the house when she was not at home. Laduna, the oldest daughter, looked after the house and the younger girls when Mahda was work-ing on the farm.

Throughout the town, everybody admired the beautiful manners and the quiet ways of Mahda's four girls. Often they received small gifts for smiling and saying "How-do" so prettily.

For a long, long time the village of Ghadiene had been troubled by a bull elephant who overturned houses, rooted

11

The bull elephant swoops up Mahda, her rice bowl, knife, and digging stick

up farm crops, and muddied the drinking water. Whenever he was hungry or vexed, the village and its people suffered from his wrath.

The old bull elephant had one torn ear, and part of one tusk was broken off. Perhaps these handicaps made him sensitive and spiteful.

One day he came to Mahda's house looking for food. Not finding any, he swooped up the three young daughters while their older sister Laduna stood screaming for help. The old elephant immediately swallowed the three girls and galloped off into the forest.

Laduna ran to the farm to get her mother. Crying and talking at the same time, she told her what the elephant had done to her sisters.

Mahda dropped everything and started to run after the elephant, but a soft voice down in the grass said, "Take your digging stick, a knife, and a bowl of food with you." Mahda and Laduna looked to see where the voice was coming from. The small head of a green cassava snake nodded at them, and then he went his way through the grass.

All the animals disliked the bull elephant not only for his meanness to human beings, but also for the dirty tricks he played on the other animals. So they were more than willing to help Mahda find the hateful beast.

She went to the house and got a bowl of cooked rice and a large kitchen knife and started out with her digging stick. She left Laduna to take care of the house and the farm while she was gone.

On through the bush went Mahda asking every bird, animal, or snake she met, "Have you seen an elephant

12

with a torn ear and a broken tusk? He has eaten my three children and I must find him at once."

Leopard spoke up at once with very clear directions: "He is sleeping under the big tree down by the river. Go quietly, girl, for he is a mean one."

Mahda hurried to the river, the birds and monkeys showing her the way. Sure enough, there was the old bull elephant snoring and groaning in his sleep. His stomach was so full and tight, that it seemed about to burst.

In her anger, Mahda forgot her fear and punched the elephant mightily with her digging stick to wake him.

"You ate my children! You ate my children! You mean old devil. Give them back to me!" Mahda screamed at him.

The screaming and the sharp punch from the stick woke the elephant. He stood up. The sight of Mahda waving a knife at him made him angry. So he swung his trunk around her waist, threw her into his mouth, rice bowl, knife, and digging stick, too!

Down, down into the great dark stomach went Mahda, whirling in and out of big and little places, until she came to rest inside the huge cavity of his stomach. As she looked around, she saw there were goats, dogs, monkeys, grown people, and huddled together in a corner, were her three children.

The children's clothes and faces were wet, but they were unharmed. When they saw their mother with a bowl of rice, right away they said they were hungry. So did all the other animals and people inside the elephant's stomach. Mahda tried to divide the rice so that each would have a small mouthful, but there just wasn't enough.

13

"But why," asked Mahda, "are you so hungry down here when there is meat all around you?" With her knife she cut large portions of the elephant's stomach and cooked them right then and there. In a short time everybody was chewing away on a piece of the roasted meat.

The smoke and heat from Mahda's fire inside his stomach made the elephant choke and cough. He got up and tried to get to the river. The heat and smoke poured from his trunk, mouth, and ears. He started to bellow because the burning pain inside his stomach was getting too strong for him to bear.

The sight of the bull elephant blowing smoke frightened and delighted the forest animals. Because he had done harm to most of them at one time or another, not one of them tried to help him. As he lumbered toward the river, his bellowing and belching grew louder and louder. With one final bellow he fell dead on the sand.

Inside his stomach, Mahda took her knife and cut a hole through the layers and layers of the elephant's stomach fat. With a steady hand, she led her children out one by one. After they were safely outside, the children helped the animals and the old people climb out.

When the village people saw what a brave thing Mahda had done for the sake of her children, they brought her fine gifts of food, clothing, and money. This was their way of saying thank you for getting rid of the troublesome beast.

Mahda's greatest honor came when the Chief gave Mahda a home in his compound, where she and her children would be loved and respected for their bravery and kindness.

Big Bird Palaver

(Ghana)

Far away in the deep, dark forest, a big gray bird lived in a kola nut tree. This bird was so mean that he ate pepper in between meals so that his meanness would always show. He never had a pleasant word for any other bird, and he could not stand to share any of the kola nuts with man or animal.

One day, the sly and tricky lizard decided to climb the tree to get a few nuts. Big Bird saw him coming and waited until Lizard reached out to pick a few choice nuts, then, Swoosh!—he threw a handful of pepper into Lizard's eyes. With a loud yell of great pain, Lizard fell to the ground. Holding his eyes, he ran blindly to the water hole and let the cool water soothe his burning eyes.

After a bit, Lizard got up and went to town. His first thought was to tell everybody about the pepper, but on second thought he kept his mouth shut.

Coming toward him from the bush was Black Deer,

15

walking proudly with her two young ones. Lizard called her to him.

"I know where there is a fine kola nut tree. Would you care to come and pick some? They are by far the choicest and sweetest nuts in the forest."

Black Deer agreed to go with Lizard, for such a delicious treat sounded very tempting on such a hot day. So, sending her young ones back home, Black Deer joined Lizard. Happily they chatted as they walked to the kola tree. During all this chattering, Lizard did not breathe one word about Big Bird in the tree, or the terrible pepper.

When they got to the tree, Lizard told Black Deer to climb up and help herself. Deer did so. In the top of the tree sat Big Bird, just sitting and waiting with his pepper. As Deer came up the tree, she looked straight into Big Bird's eyes. Neither one said a word. Without blinking an eye, Big Bird took a handful of pepper and threw it into Deer's eyes. Crying in pain, she fell to the ground.

Do you think Lizard tried to help her? Oh, no, that sneaky coward took a big stick and beat Deer as she lay on the ground. The pepper was burning Deer's eyes so badly that she could not see. She begged for help, but Lizard kept raining blows on her with his big stick, until Black Deer was dead. With the coldness of a monster, Lizard cut up the deer and took the meat home to his family.

With the same cunning, Lizard went back to the forest path a few days later to find another foolish animal. Sure enough, along came Red Monkey just as frisky as you please.

"Come, let us go and pick kola nuts, little red one,"

16

said the sly, smooth-talking Lizard. Liking kola nuts very much, Red Monkey went along. Upon Lizard's suggestions, he climbed the tree where Big Bird was sitting. Poor little Red Monkey did not get the chance to pick one nut before he got pepper in his eyes. Howling like a banshee, Red Monkey fell to the ground.

Picking up a stick, Lizard struck the little monkey so many hard blows that he quivered and died with his eyes open, looking toward Lizard for help. As with Black Deer, he cut up Red Monkey and took the meat home to his family. In this mean way, many animals were killed by Lizard.

Some weeks later, Lizard felt he had to try his trick once again. So back to the path he went.

On this fine sunny day along came pygmy Antelope galloping in and out between the trees. Lizard invited him to come and pick kola nuts with him. Little did Lizard know that Antelope was not only wise, but cautious of such friendliness from a lowly lizard. Having a secret plan in mind, Antelope went with Lizard to the kola nut tree.

Near the tree he noticed the tracks of many animals coming to the tree, but no tracks going away from the tree. Antelope was thinking that something strange was going on under this tree, or else something up in that tree was eating animals. So when Lizard invited Antelope to climb the tree he said, "Lizard, this kola tree is your tree, and you must know where the best nuts are. Suppose you climb up first to show me the way."

In all his crafty thinking, Lizard had never expected this, but in order to save face he began to climb. As he climbed he tried to dodge and hide from Big Bird sitting up in the tree. He was hoping that Big Bird might be asleep, or away from the tree, but not so. There as big as the sun sat Big Bird with his bag of pepper.

No sooner had Lizard reached the highest limb, than Big Bird let him have the whole bag of pepper. But Lizard had brought along some pepper also, and he let Big Bird have pepper right back in his face.

Down to the ground howling and screaming fell Big Bird and Lizard in a shower of kola nuts. Antelope, fearing for his life, jumped on Big Bird and killed him. Lizard was knocked unconscious by the fall. With no one to disturb him, Antelope stuffed as many nuts as he could in his two pockets.

When Lizard could open his eyes, he turned to Antelope and said, "You know, you've killed a very special bird, and there will be palaver over his unnatural death. We must do something, and do it quickly."

So, together, they dug a hole and buried Big Bird.

Turning to Antelope, Lizard said, "Now, give me all the nuts you picked up, and I will tell no one about the death of Big Bird." Foolishly, Antelope gave him all of his nuts, and even picked up a few more. Anything to keep Lizard from telling about his bad deed!

Having smoothed the ground over Big Bird's grave, they went back to town with sealed lips.

When the sun went down, Lizard went back to the burial hole and took Big Bird out. He carried the dead bird to his wife and told her to cook it. Then he went outside and tied a rope around his leg and told his wife, "When the bird is done, pull on this rope and I will come to eat."

While Lizard sat pleasuring himself in the cool of the palm tree, Antelope came along and saw the rope. He thought about it for a minute. Seeing that Lizard was asleep, he untied the rope from Lizard's leg and tied it around his own.

Moving a short distance away from Lizard, Antelope sat down to see what might happen.

In a little while he felt someone pulling on the rope, and his leg jerked. He got up and followed the rope into Lizard's house. It was so dark and smoky inside the house that Antelope could not see Lizard's wife, nor could she see him.

"Come, husband, here is your rice and meat. Eat good." Antelope ate every grain of rice and cleaned every shred of meat from the bird's bones. When he finished, he went back outside to rest from such a fine meal. In the meantime, Lizard woke up and felt hungry. So he went to see if the bird was cooked.

"Wife, are the meat and rice ready?"

"What meat and rice? I just gave you all the bird and rice. You ate it all. Why do you come looking for more?" asked his exasperated wife.

"This is the first time I have been in this house since I brought the dead bird home. Now, who did you give my food to?"

Casually, Antelope strolled in and said, "Your wife gave your nicely cooked bird to me, and I ate it all. She thought it was you in this smoky kitchen. So don't humbug her. I just paid you back for the dirty trick you played on me. As for killing Big Bird, the Chief will take care of you for that."

The Chief talked the bird palaver over with his councillors, and they decided that Lizard's tongue should be spliced at the end for his lying, and that his teeth should be taken away, so that he could eat no more kola nuts. Lizard's shame was so great that he hid himself under a stone.

Although Lizard still climbs up and down trees, he hasn't tried to make friends with a bird, nor has he eaten a kola nut since that long-ago time.

Woman Humbug Too Much

(Ghana)

Once upon a time, a fine hunter by the name of Afiah had a bad-mouth woman for a wife. All day long she fussed, complained, nagged, and criticized. Not only did she have a bad mouth, but her cooking was bad also. Even the house and the children were dirty, because the lazy wife Welu spent her time complaining.

Each day Afiah went to the forest to hunt for meat to feed his family. When he made a good kill, Welu said he should have brought more. When he did not get any meat, she called him weak and lazy. Nothing ever satisfied her.

Constantly her tongue wagged: "I work, work, all day while you sit in the forest and sleep. My back and my fingers are worn out with all the housework. You better find a second wife to help me, or I will surely die."

Afiah did not answer Welu. He knew it was no use. Immediately he started on his search for a second wife.

From village to village he went seeking an unmarried girl. Everywhere he went he got the same answer. All the women had husbands and the young girls turned their heads away from his proposal. Afiah was a poor man and did not have the price of a new bride. So he was turned down by all.

With a heavy heart Afiah came back to his house with no second wife. This vexed Welu greatly and she abused him with many shameful words. Throughout their village she spoiled his name by saying, "Afiah is a no-good husband. His empty head holds no brains, and his body has no power. For my part, he is as simple and soft as a woman."

The bitter words of Welu made Afiah the laughing stock of the village. Even when he wasn't hunting, he would walk far into the forest to get away from the sound of Welu's harsh voice. To be scolded in his house was one thing, but to be shamed in front of the whole village was too much.

One evening as he sat under a cottonwood tree, he talked out loud to himself: "I need a good, kind woman in my house. Someone to do some fine cooking and tend the children. My Welu is so mean that my heart and body ache with so much scolding and humbugging. It is better to lie down in death than to live this miserable life with bad-mouth Welu."

As Afiah was talking to himself, one of the Forest Spirits heard him. Thinking to herself that she could do him a good favor, she turned herself into a monkey and spoke to him: "See, I am a monkey."

Afiah binds second wife Tabe to him with a white kola nut

"Yes, I see that you are a monkey," replied Afiah. "What is that to me? Monkeys are everywhere."

"But I can be something else other than a monkey!" exclaimed the Forest Spirit.

"What else?" asked Afiah, not really believing anything he was hearing or seeing. "Once a monkey, always a monkey."

"Not so," said the Spirit. "You must please wait small."

Quick, quick, the Monkey Spirit shook all over, and ever so slowly there appeared before Afiah a fine young maiden.

Afiah rubbed his eyes. Could this be true? A monkey one minute, and a girl the next? Yet the sight of such a beautiful creature melted his cold heart and warm love flooded his body. Immediately, he asked her to be his wife.

She agreed, "I will be your wife for true, but I fear that you may shame me by telling your people that I am really a monkey."

"I swear on my life that I will never tell your secret. Be my wife and my mouth is sealed."

"If you ever tell my secret, I will leave your house at once. Now, give me a white kola nut that will bind us in marriage."

Afiah found a kola nut and gave it to her. She put the nut in a small bag and hung it around her neck. "Husband, my bush name is Kahn, but my so-so name is Tabe, so that is what you must call me."

When they reached his house, Afiah called out to Welu. "This girl has agreed to be my second wife. Do

24

not abuse or humbug her. She is young and soft, so do not show her your hard mean ways."

"Where did you get her?" asked first wife Welu.

"She comes from a far-off place," answered Afiah. He could not, and would not, tell Welu where he had found Tabe, and Tabe did not let a word pass her teeth. He also knew that Welu would not let the matter rest. Her mind and her tongue were too sharp for that.

Welu, as first wife, gave Tabe her chores and her place to sleep. Tabe had to do the cooking, tend the farm, do the washing, make the market, and care for the children. And what tasks did Welu save for herself? None, absolutely none. As Tabe performed each chore Welu followed, speaking scornful words and scolding her. Nothing was ever done right. Always cross, cross words. Yet, Tabe never uttered a harsh word.

Each night when Afiah returned from his hunting trip, Welu asked him, "Where did you find your second wife?" Always she got the same answer. "She came from a far-off place."

Jealousy and curiosity were gnawing holes in Welu's mind. So one evening she fixed palm wine and gave it to Afiah. "Drink it all," she said. Surprised at Welu's kindness, he drank the wine quickly.

While Afiah's head was swimming with the wine, Welu softly asked him, "Where did you find second wife?"

Feeling light-headed and full of wine, Afiah told everything. "Tabe was a monkey in the forest and changed herself into a girl. She promised to be my wife if I would never tell her secret. You must never let her know or else she will go away."

"Her secret is safe with me," said Welu. But she didn't mean it. She was going to bide her time.

One day as Tabe sat eating her bowl of rice, Welu came over and kicked it over. Then she screamed at her, "Pick up every grain of that rice, you clumsy ninny." Tabe said not a word and picked up all the rice.

"Come here," commanded Welu. "Scratch my back." Tabe gently scratched her back.

"Now, wipe my breath from the air." Tabe's cup was full—"But how can I wipe your breath from the air?"

"You fool of a monkey," screamed Welu. "I work, work, work all day, and you sit around sleeping and plaiting your hair. My husband was weak for a pretty face, but I know for true what you really are—A SIMPLE MONKEY!"

Tabe knew Afiah had given her secret away. With one long, loud cry she ran straight to the forest and never looked back.

When Afiah came home, he looked for Tabe to bring him his food.

"Woman, where is second wife?" Sweetly, Welu replied, "She is gone to the forest. She likes to sit under the cottonwood tree and rest herself. Her lazy ways are a hard thing for me to bear."

Afiah knew something was wrong. Tabe did not have a lazy bone in her body. Quickly he went to the bush looking and calling for Tabe.

Near a gree-gree tree he found a white kola. Loudly

26

he asked, "Whose kola nut is this?" Again, louder, he asked, "Whose kola nut is this?" No answer came.

Afiah knew something bad had happened to his beauti-ful Tabe. With anger in his heart, he went back home and struck Welu a heavy blow with his cutlass. She fell dead with a mean smile on her face.

Time after time, Afiah went to the forest seeking Tabe. He asked all the monkeys, but they only laughed and cracked nuts. They didn't know or understand any "man" words. The beautiful Tabe was never found.

Alone, sad, and heart-broken, Afiah wandered in the forest until he died.

Since that time man has not taken a monkey for a wife.

Frog's Strange Power

(Ghana)

Kafi, the son of Gombawe, lived with his mother and three sisters in the small village of Addah. The people of Addah were worshipers of the sky gods Sun and Moon.

Now that Kafi had finished his year in the secret bush society, his family was ready to discuss marriage with Kafi's intended bride.

His family had selected their second cousin's eligible daughter, but Kafi, in his independent way, announced that he was not going to marry any girl from his own tribe. Upsetting his parents further, he proclaimed that his bride must be the daughter of the Sun and the Moon.

The cheeky young Kafi would not listen to any of the offers proposed by his uncles, the village elders, or his grandfather. He insisted that his bride must be the only daughter of the powerful sky gods, and no other.

Not wishing to shame himself further, Gombawe sent for his favorite servants. He asked them to carry Kafi's

28

marriage proposal up to the Sun and the Moon. Each servant on pain of death refused to go on such a dangerous journey.

Papa Gombawe continued to ask his friends and male relatives to carry his son's message. No one would agree. Getting vexed with Kafi and his marriage business, Gombawe told Kafi to find his own messenger.

So Kafi put his foot on the path that led to the thick bush. As he came across his many animal friends, he asked for their help. They looked at him in disbelief. Tamba, the leopard, told him, "You are reaching too far, young one. The sky people are not your kind. Leave them be."

Kafi would not take no for an answer. His heart and mind were set on the greatness that such a marriage would bring to his house. Selfishly, he was thinking, "Who but the son of Gombawe could obtain such an illustrious bride."

After asking every animal and bird he met, and getting all nays, Kafi sat down to think about what he should do to get his message up to the Sun and the Moon.

While he was resting, a large green frog hopped up to him. "Greetings, my friend. The sad look on your face tells me that you are troubled. May I help you? My legs are long and my voice loud. I can do many things. Give me a chance to prove myself."

Kafi told Frog his problem. He had to get someone to carry his marriage proposal to Nyanna, the only daughter of the great gods Sun and Moon. Readily, Frog agreed to help Kafi.

Frog, in his many travels throughout the land, had seen

girls come down from the sky on spider webs. Each girl carried a large jar to draw water from a certain well.

Thinking only of helping his friend, Frog hid by the well, and when the girls came down, he jumped into one of the jars and was carried to the Sun.

Just as soon as the girl got up to the Sun and put her jar down, Frog jumped out and presented himself to the great god Sun.

"O powerful and great King, Ruler of all the Heavens, Giver of Life and Death, hear my humble message. I bring the heart and love of my friend Kafi Gknamee Magah, who desires marriage with your beautiful daughter Nyanna."

Sun listened patiently. After consulting with his wife the Moon, he agreed to accept Kafi's proposal, their first stipulation being that Kafi come himself and bring the first part of the bride price.

Frog waited until the serving girls were ready to come to earth for water. Then into one of the jars jumped Frog for his return trip.

He gave Kafi the good news that his proposal had been accepted. Frog also told him that he would have to take a bag of gold himself up to Sun as a bond of good faith and evidence of his earthly wealth.

Kafi collected the required bag of gold and sent Frog back to heaven with it. He refused to go himself, not knowing how he could climb a spider web. Kafi also told Frog he must bring Nyanna down on his return.

Again, Frog traveled to heaven in one of the water

Nyanna's serving girls come down from the sky on a spider's web

jars. This time he did not go in to see Sun, but hid himself in Nyanna's room.

While she was sleeping, Frog hopped over to her bed and stole both her eyes. Nyanna's loud screams brought Sun and Moon to her room. When they saw what had happened, they sent for the palace "diviner."

The wise old diviner knew right away that a suitor had cast a spell on Nyanna. In such cases, the old man reasoned, the girl should be sent to the young man or else she would die.

In order to save his daughter's life, Sun gave a royal order that all spiders in his kingdom should immediately spin a strong web capable of taking Nyanna safely to earth.

As the spiders spun the web, Frog followed them. When they finished the last thread, Frog ran ahead of the others straight to Kafi.

"She's coming, she's coming. The beautiful Nyanna is coming," croaked Frog. He didn't tell Kafi that he had stolen her eyes and that Nyanna would have to be led down the web.

As Nyanna came down the web, there was a shaft of strange white light and two serving girls to lead her safely down. Coming quickly to her side, Frog gave Nyanna back her eyes and led her to Kafi. With much feasting and dancing, Kafi and Nyanna were married. Her parents did not attend the wedding, or did they send any goodwill gift to the groom's parents. Knowing that she had incurred their wrath, Nyanna never visited her parents again.

As for Kafi's friend, the Frog, Sun and Moon have

constantly punished him for taking their daughter's eyes. During the day the hot angry Sun burns his skin, and at night the cold blue light of the Moon lights the way so that man can find the frog and kill him.

Even during a rainstorm, if you look up, you may be able to see frogs climbing down the giant spider web that leads from sky to earth. This is really the only power that Frog has. If he tells you otherwise, don't believe him.

Binyoka, the Old Woman of the Water

(Ivory Coast)

In the far-distant village of Magashe lived the Tambauu family. According to village law, each family had to give seven days' work on the rice farms each month. Keeping the hundreds of birds away from the budding rice is hard, lonely work. Since each family shares in the rice when it is harvested, each family must also share in tending the farm.

When it came the Tambauu family's week, Mama Sai sent Hallah, her only daughter, and Hallah's brother Boto.

From sunup until sundown, Hallah and Boto sat at the edge of the field chucking rocks and swishing branches at the pesky birds. The hot sun, flies, mosquitoes, and loneliness made the work the most undesirable in the whole village.

One day Hallah and Boto could stand the heat no longer. They went down to the lake to get a drink of

34

Hallah meets Binyoka in her
underwater home

water. They didn't mean to stay very long, but the cool shade and the cool water made them tarry a bit. When they got back to the rice field, the birds had picked every blade of rice from the farm and were still swarming over the bare field.

Hallah's heart stood still. What would her mother do to her? What would the Chief do to her family? She and Boto would be severely punished, for a spoiled rice crop meant hunger during the rainy season. Because they had put their personal comfort ahead of their duty the whole village would suffer.

Fearing the village wrath and her mother's anger, Hallah ran to the lake and threw herself in. Boto heard the big splash and ran to help his sister. He was too late; just as he got to the water's edge, he saw Hallah's head disappear below the water.

Boto ran screaming to the village, "Mama, come quick, the water has swallowed Hallah."

The whole village followed Boto and his family to the lake. He pointed to the place he had seen Hallah disappear. Now there were only small ripples quietly flowing along. Two young men dived in to find her, but they gave up after their third try.

Down at the bottom of the lake, Hallah had reached the land of the Nijji people (water spirits).

As she walked around this strange underwater world, she came to a house that belonged to Binyoka, the chief priestess of the water spirits. She is sometimes called the "old woman of the water," for both her good and bad deeds.

It is said that whenever there is a boat accident, Binyoka takes all the good people from the boat. The chosen ones live with her, while the other passengers are left to float until their bodies are found.

Binyoka saw Hallah wandering near her house and called to her, "Come, my child, and sit with me. My house is your home now. Do not be afraid; there will be no punishment for you down here."

Strangely, Hallah did not fear the old woman, nor did she feel out of place in this mysterious world. Her head felt a little dizzy, and her legs a little wobbly, but otherwise nothing seemed very different.

Hallah entered the old woman's house and did the chores she was assigned. Every day there were different people to meet. All of them seemed to know about Hallah and her family. A great many of the water people came by Binyoka's house to leave gifts or money. Some wanted the old woman to reach up to the water and bring one of the earth people down to visit.

Hallah never saw any children or any member of her family. As time passed, she grew sad and homesick. One day she asked Binyoka if she could go back to her home on earth. For a moment, Binyoka hid her face behind her long thin fingers.

"Because you have been kind and have not asked troublesome questions, I will reward you." Placing two giant pots in front of her, Binyoka said, "Which one would you like, little Hallah, the clay pot or the iron pot?"

Hallah chose the iron one. As she struggled to lift it,

she stumbled, and the contents spilled. Gold and diamonds of every description fell all around her. "Take all of it, my child. You will need it for your dowry. In my mind I see your husband. His name is Tamba. You must marry him and no other. If you choose another, all of this will disappear," said the old woman.

Covered with gold and diamonds, Hallah came up to the top of the water. Seeing no one around, she sat down on the shore to think on her happiness.

Far down the beach, two fishermen saw the beautiful Hallah sitting alone. They spread the news of the girl on the beach covered with gold and diamonds.

From far and near, young and old suitors came seeking marriage with the beautiful and rich Hallah. As each man presented himself, she listened carefully as he gave his name, waiting to hear the name Tamba.

Many warriors, hunters, and sons of kings came to make their proposals. Hallah refused them all.

One day a tall, handsome hunter with a lame leg presented himself to Hallah.

"My name is Tamba," he said. Hallah's face lighted up. This was the name of the husband the old woman had told her to find.

The whole town was so overjoyed that they prepared a most wonderful feast for the bridal couple. As the wedding ceremony was taking place, the lame leg of Tamba was cured and he walked without a limp.

Hallah used her gold and diamonds to buy many goats and cows. In their village, Hallah and Tamba were now rich indeed, for wealth is judged by the number of cattle a family possesses. But such wealth made the other families jealous.

One day while Tamba was hunting in the bush, a spear was thrown through his heart. He fell dead from the wound.

Hallah was bowed down with grief. Having no one to turn to, she went to the lake seeking the counsel and comfort of old Binyoka.

Binyoka told her, "Go to the place where Tamba's body lies and put one of your gold bangles on his arm." Hallah did this immediately. Then she commanded her servants to bring Tamba's body back to their house. Hiding in the house was Binyoka. She used her magic power and brought Tamba back to life. Before Hallah or Tamba could thank the old woman she disappeared. All they saw was a small puddle of water where she had stood.

The jealous villagers, thinking that Tamba was dead, came to gather up all of their cattle. They were surprised to find Tamba standing guard with his spear ready by his side. With loud, cowardly cries they fled. Binyoka led the fleeing enemies straight to the lake, where they tumbled headlong into the water.

With the evil, jealous villagers out of the way, Hallah and Tamba lived in wealth and happiness all their days. They blessed their village with many good deeds.

When there was hunger, they provided food. When there was sadness, they brought good words.

The old people say that kindness begets kindness, and Hallah received her due share.

The Snake's New Skin

(Ghana)

A long, long time ago, the Ga people say that the first family on earth was told that they would never die. Nyame, the sky god, told them that their old skin would be replaced by new skin when their death time came.

Nyame had made the first people from three balls of clay. With a little breeze from each of the four winds he put breath in them, and with a handful of heat from the sun he warmed their bodies.

These first people lived without clothes, houses, or fire. They wandered wherever the fruits and nuts were plenti' ful. There was no worry, hurry, grief, sadness, or bad' ness. The Great Nyame took care of them.

In order to keep his promise of new skin to the people, Nyame chose man's best friend, the dog, as the carrier. Wrapped in a neat parcel, the skins were given to Dog. He was to make the journey down to earth and back alone. Nyame wanted to be sure that Dog would have nothing to distract his attention from his important mission.

Halfway down to earth, Dog caught the smell of meat cooking over the open fires. He was overcome with curiosity and hunger. As he came down to earth he put down the parcel and ran over to join his friends in their evening meal. For the moment, he forgot the warning Nyame had given: "Do not stop until you safely deliver the skins."

While Dog was eating, Sheep asked him, "What are you carrying in your parcel, Friend Dog?"

"I have some very important things in that parcel. The Supreme One asked me to take these skins to the first 'man' family. They will use them when Death comes to get them."

Dog did not know it, but Snake overheard him, and Snake wanted a new skin so that he would never die. He wasted no time in slipping the parcel under his stomach and crawling far away from the other animals.

Opening the parcel, he took out the three skins and gave one to each member of his own family.

After Dog finished eating, he reached down to pick up his parcel. He was shocked to find it gone. He was too afraid to go back to Nyame, so he went on to find Man and tell him the skins had been stolen.

Man begged Nyame for more skins, but he would not agree to send more. "I gave you a chance for ever-lasting life, but your friend Dog spoiled it with his greedy mouth. So, from now on, you and Dog will die when your time comes. And as for Snake, he will be killed by man if he comes near him. For his thievery, snake will crawl on his stomach and eat dust."

41

With those words Nyame disappeared into the clouds and man has not seen him since.

Snake did not mind Nyame's words, for he and his family had the new skins. Once a year Snake changes his old skin for a new new one, while Man dies because Dog's hunger got the best of him.

The Fetish Priest

(Ghana)

In the village of Owangarra, the people wanted to cut a road to the neighboring town of Salala. Before the road building could get under way, the "diviner" had to make the proper ritual of "pouring cold water," and knocking the earth so that the work would go smoothly.

Many of the old, old Akan people in Owangarra believed in the god Bayo, whose spirit lived in the giant mahogany tree. This special tree was a very important fetish for the old ones. "It cannot be chopped or moved without asking its permission," they muttered to each other. "We will see, we will see."

Ashong, a master builder, was given the task of cutting the road. He demanded that each family send its boys and young men to cut the bush.

All was going well until they came to the last stretch of forest near the Salala border. Here the trees were thick and tall. Seeing the men fall with fever and exhaustion,

Ashong sent for more men. It did indeed seem strange that such strong, brave men should fall like children just when the road was almost completed. A sickening fear seemed to have come over the workers.

Ashong went to investigate. "Baas, come, I will show you the trouble," said Farifa, one of the workers. "See that tree: it has strong ju-ju, we cannot get it to move."

"But why?" asked Ashong. "You have over a hundred strong men and plenty of rope. Let me see this tree."

He walked over to the partly cleared road. Standing in the middle of the clearing, all by itself, was one lone tree. It was a magnificent mahogany, but not as large as some of the trees they had pulled down the past few days. Not one of the Owangarra workers would touch that tree. They just sat with their heads turned away.

Because Ashong was not one of the Akan people, there was much he did not understand about their customs. Farifa told him: "That tree is the house of the spirit Bayo, and for the people it is their special fetish. Not one of these men will chop or move that tree before the Fetish Priest comes and performs the proper ceremonies."

"Well then, Farifa, hurry and get the priest and bring him back here at once. I need his help," said Ashong impatiently.

When the Priest came, he looked up at the tree and then bowed his head with respect. Then he turned to Ashong, and asked, "You have need of my services?"

"Indeed I do," answered Ashong. "Will you ask the tree to forgive my ignorance. I did not know this tree was the home of the spirit Bayo."

The Priest agreed to talk to the tree. Gently, he tapped

44

the tree's trunk, and quietly he talked to it for a short while as he lovingly caressed its rough bark. Then he said to Ashong: "The spirit Bayo has agreed to move and make his home in another tree, but there are some things I will need."

After clearing his throat and pausing, the Priest said, "I will need three young lambs and two bottles of gin for the ceremony. The blood of the lambs will soothe the cuts your axes will make in its trunk, and the gin will purify any evil spirits that might have ventured near the tree."

Taking off his robe, the Priest slit the throat of each lamb and allowed the warm blood to run onto the roots of the tree. Then he opened the gin and poured some around the ground, and up and down the trunk of the sacred tree. While he poured the gin he chanted in a sing-song voice, "O Great and Powerful Spirit, the house you live in stands in the way of the people's new road. I beg you to please leave this tree and go to another. Do not punish anyone for their ignorance of your presence. I promise you that the people of Owangarra will always show their gratitude and respect. On the eve of each new moon they will make a suitable sacrifice of their choicest meat, food, and drink. The young men who work on this road will see to it."

More gin was poured around the base of the tree and the Fetish Priest went into a frenzied dance as he circled the tree. Gasping for breath, he stopped in front of Ashong and told him, "You may now move the tree, but my services will cost you one pouch of gold nuggets."

Farifa gave the Priest the gold, and then he put one small rope around the tree, and with one jerk by the workers, the huge mahogany came out of the ground, roots and all.

The Priest put on his robe, pocketed his pouch of gold, and showed the workers the cottonwood tree in the bush that was the new home of the tree spirit.

When the road was completed the towns of Owangarra and Salala celebrated with a great feast, but before they dined the workers offered the choicest food, meat, and drink to the tree spirit in its new home.

Thus it was proved that every living thing has a spirit, and that spirits must be shown proper respect by both believers and nonbelievers.

A Lover's Riddle

(Ivory Coast)

Owusu was the finest and strongest warrior in the king-dom of Tahda. Wherever he went, young girls looked at him with soft loving eyes, and other young men looked at him with envy. For all his bravery and handsome good looks, Owusu had one weakness: he could not easily make up his mind.

For many months he had been paying court to a girl in Tahda and a girl in the town of Sewor. Each girl's father wanted Owusu to make his marriage intentions known. Now, this was his problem: he loved both girls equally and could not decide which one he should take for his wife. He knew this was dangerous business, but he was enjoying himself so much that he did not wish to marry just now.

On the first Thursday after the new moon, the towns of Tahda and Sewor were holding their female secret society ceremonies. Owusu wanted to pleasure himself at both affairs, because both girls were expecting him.

As he came to the fork in the path, he sat down and talked to himself. "If I take this path, I will please Niena, but if I take the other path, I will please Aisata. What must I do? I will lose one or the other, for I cannot be in two places at one time. It is better for me to die in happiness than to live in disappointment." So he picked up a poison fruit and ate it. Death took him slowly to Dead Town.

Back in the two towns, the girls, Niena and Aisata, waited for Owusu. As the evening wore on, each girl decided to go and look for him.

Niena was the first to reach the place where Owusu lay dead. At the sight of the handsome warrior, Niena cried out loudly in her grief, "O cruel death, you have taken my one true love. My life is finished, I cannot live without Owusu."

Seeing the remainder of the poison fruit beside Owusu, Niena ate it and fell dead beside him.

Much later, Aisata came searching for Owusu. When she came to the place where Owusu lay, her grieving was loud and hard. But when she saw Niena lying beside Owusu, she fell into a deep faint.

After Aisata got herself together, she went to consult Okeipu, the diviner. She wanted him to make a strong "medicine" to bring Owusu back to life. For such strong "ju-ju," Aisata had to "dash" Okeipu three cows and three goats. Then he sent her away while he set about making the proper medicine.

Taking some leaves from the poison fruit tree, he

crushed the juice from them and put it in a snail shell. Then he took a sharp knife and made a cut over Owusu's heart and poured some of the leaf juice in the hole. He did the same thing to Niena's body. While he waited for the "medicine" to work, he called Aisata to come and watch.

"Look smart, girl, see the boy's fingers moving. See the girl blinking her eyes. The medicine is working," said Okeipu the diviner. He stood over the bodies and chanted, "Dead no more, dead no more. Rise up and face the poison fruit tree. You are dead no more."

Owusu and Niena stood up; old man Death had turned them loose. The two girls looked at each other, and then looked at Owusu. He was still fine, strong and handsome. Both girls still wanted him for a husband. But Owusu just stood looking from one girl to the other, not brave enough to choose one and reject the other.

Aisata asked him, "Which one of us will you take for your wife? Both of us have proved our love."

Now this is the riddle Owusu had to answer—Niena had killed herself for love of him, and Aisata had brought him back to life. Which one should he choose?

Which one would you choose?

The Three Stupid Cows

(Ivory Coast)

Many, many years ago, cows lived in the bush and fought constantly with the other animals for food and water. Some of the cows realized they could not continue the vicious battles and went to live with Man in his villages.

Among one of the herds, there were three simple cow sisters. They were so stupid, and stubborn, that the other cows left them in the forest to fend for themselves.

The oldest sister had a beautiful coat of white slick fur, with one black spot on her forehead. Her curved horns had the sharpness of fine iron blades, which she used effectively whenever the sisters were attacked by other animals. Her name was Bwana.

The three sisters were very close and did everything together. Very early they had found out that no animal would tackle three cows at one time. So sticking and staying together was their best means of survival in the unfriendly jungle.

The second cow sister was a mottled brown with big white spots on her fur. Her horns were small, and were not sharp enough to help much in a fight, but her quick, stout hoofs had made many animals run for their life. This sister's name was Talu.

The youngest sister, whose name was Faji, had a soft coat of smooth black fur. Faji had one distinct feature that made her different from her sisters: *she had no horns.* Consequently, she was ridiculed and scorned by the other forest animals.

As the three sisters wandered through the forest un-protected by the herd, Leopard, Lion, and Hyena watched them with hungry eyes.

King Lion decided he would have cow meat for three meals within a fortnight. So he began to plan how he would separate the sisters and catch them one by one. He knew he could not subdue three angry cows, so he thought of ways to flatter each sister, or else to make each one jealous or suspicious of the other.

One day while Bwana, the first sister, was grazing alone, Lion sidled up to her and said, "Good day, my future queen. How nice it is to see you looking so fresh. I want to pay my respects to your great beauty and your bravery. The forest animals are most desirous of having you rule their kingdom but, of course, that would mean that you would have to leave your sisters. I am sure you would not mind that, since they make you do all the fighting and all the work. Leave those troublesome sisters and be our queen."

The meanness in Bwana's eyes melted a little as she listened, but she made no answer. Finally, she walked away and joined her sisters, chewing her cud with deliberation.

A few days later, King Lion approached the second sister and told her, "Your soft brown eyes and quiet ways hold the wisdom of the world. You should leave your jealous sisters and seek a husband who will appreciate you. Your place is on a throne beside the great Kwame. Do not tarry any longer with relatives who abuse you."

Talu was indeed flattered by such grand words, but she did not commit herself to the Lion's fancy ideas. It did occur to her that Bwana and Faji had never told her that she had beautiful eyes.

Just before twilight, King Lion found the third sister, Faji, down at the water hole. Poor Faji. Her skinny body and hornless head had made her the joke of the forest, and the Lion knew this. But his slick, greedy ways made him say, "Oh, there you are, my beautiful Faji. Did you know that you are the most unique and respected animal in the whole jungle? Your flat, hornless head makes you the most beautiful of all the cow sisters. Both of them are envious of the admiration you receive, and they are plotting to do away with you. In order to save yourself, you must leave them immediately."

Faji believed the Lion and went galloping off through the forest to get away from her sisters. She didn't get very far. The sweet-talking Lion was now her enemy. Before she could call for help, the Lion pounced on her, and had his first meal of cow meat.

Bwana and Talu searched the length of the forest for their lost sister Faji. Every animal they asked gave them the same answer, "Umm-mm," and nothing else. By now they were suspicious of each other. Each began to make excuses to get away by herself. Talu said she was going to find some sweeter grass, and perhaps look for a husband.

As she wandered alone through the tall grass, the Lion saw his chance to have his second meal of sweet cow meat. Not having anyone to help her, Talu was no match for the powerful lion. She was quickly captured and devoured.

Now only Bwana was left. With no sisters to help her, she decided to find King Lion, since he had promised to make her queen. In her haste to get to Lion's house, she didn't look to the right or left. He jumped at her throat and dragged her to his nest where all the Lion's family could share in his third meal of delicious meat.

So all three stupid cows, believing the Lion's flattery, were destroyed. Had they stayed together they could have killed the crafty beast, but separately they were no match for Lion. They learned the hard, hard way that in unity there is strength. The clever Lion knew that to divide and conquer was the perfect way to eat three stupid cow sisters.

The Man Who Scorned Spirits

(Ivory Coast)

At the edge of the town of Niani, there was a small plot of uncultivated land that was said to be the private property of the forest spirits. Many reports of strange mid-night ceremonies held on the small plot had been told and retold by the townspeople. Consequently, no one would dare offend the spirits by planting or cutting any shrub on the sacred plot.

However, there was a certain man by the name of Flumo, who decided that he would make a farm on the "taboo" piece of land. He laughed and mocked the people when they begged him not to touch the sacred land of the spirits. Flumo's indifference showed that he had no respect for the spirits, or for the advice of his elders.

With the pleas of his friends still ringing in his ears, the hard-headed Flumo went ahead with his plan to make a farm on the spirits' land.

On the first clear day, he cut some of the bushes, and

went home to rest. The next morning when he went back to the field, he found *all* the bushes cut. Thinking nothing was amiss, he rejoiced in his good fortune.

On the following morning, he went back to the farm and cut down one tree, and went home. When he returned to cut the remaining trees, he found that *all* the trees had been cut down.

"I am the happiest and luckiest of men," exclaimed Flumo as he ran through the village embracing his friends.

"Come and see my farm. The shrub is cleared and the trees are down. The forest spirits are my slaves. They have done all the hard work for me. You foolish people have been sitting here starving while good farm land sits idle. See how the spirits are helping me."

The townspeople grunted in their throats and said nothing. They knew that the vengeance of the spirits was slow but sure. So they waited.

Flumo continued to cultivate the piece of land. He lit a small fire to burn off the stumps and hard grasses. As usual, he went home to rest. During the night, the fire evenly cleaned the field, and put itself out.

At sunrise, Flumo told his wife, "Take this one grain of corn and plant it, then leave this basket of corn seeds in the middle of the field, and let's see what happens." By morning, sure enough, all the corn seeds were planted throughout the field.

Weeks passed and the corn ripened. Joyfully, Flumo took his cutlass and cut down one corn stalk, and went home, counting in his head the money he would make from his abundant crop.

When he returned the next day, *all* the corn had been

harvested and taken away. Not one single stalk was left in the field. Nor were there any footprints leading to or from the field. Quickly, Flumo ran through the village crying, "Thief, thief, someone has stolen my corn." No one turned an ear to listen to his wild tale, for he had been warned not to touch the sacred property of the spirits.

With a heavy heart he went home and found that his house had fallen in, and his wife and children had dis-appeared. Alone and friendless, Flumo wandered off into the deep forest and was never seen or heard from again.

Thus it was that man paid dearly for his disrespect to the land of the spirits, and for ignoring the advice of his elders.

Fire's Unfriendly Visit

(Ghana)

Many, many years ago along the west coast of Africa, Fire was regarded as a great spirit sent from the sky to rule the earth people. Fire was feared, respected, and worshiped. Its magical properties were too great for Man to ask why and how come. No one dared come too near Fire without asking permission, and those who did not show the proper respect suffered from Fire's anger.

During those long-ago days, the cunning, crafty Leopard decided to make friends with Fire. It was his idea to discover the secret of the Fire Spirit's great power.

Each day after hunting for food in the bush, Leopard would stop by Fire's house for a visit.

"I say there, good friend, have you tasted the palm nuts this season? They are exceedingly sweet."

Fire sat on his holy seat and answered Leopard not a word.

Leopard tried again to make conversation. "I know

57

where there are some delicious crayfish. Would you like to come along?"

Fire stood up and said, "I bid you, excuse me. It is time for my evening walk."

The great Fire Spirit wanted no part of Leopard's friendship. Still, Leopard was not discouraged. Each eve-ning, before or after supper, he came to visit Fire, and received the same cool welcome.

Leopard's wife began to wonder about this strange friendship her husband bragged about. He was always visiting Fire, but not once did Fire come to their house. The wife thought it was because their children were not always respectful. So she chastised the little ones about their manners. Still Fire did not come.

Leopard's wife thought perhaps their house was not fine enough for Fire to visit. So she humbugged Leopard to build a new house for them. This he did.

Leopard again went to visit Fire. "I beg you, Great Fire, do me the honor of a visit to my new home. My wife will give me no peace if you do not come."

As Fire listened to Leopard's whining voice he sus-pected some kind of trick, because Leopard was so insis-tent. Fire told him, "I will visit your house if you will provide me with a path of dry leaves. My feet are very tender, and the hard bare ground gives me much pain."

"O great spirit, if you will honor my lowly house, I will place the dry leaves all the way from your house to mine," Leopard replied.

Quickly he ran to tell his wife the good news: "Fire

Fire comes to visit Leopard's house

is coming to visit us." So the wife agreed to help Leopard gather the leaves to put on the path. Feeling proud that her husband's friend was coming for a visit, she prepared much food and wine to welcome their honored guest.

The Leopards sat down to wait for Fire's coming. All was in readiness.

Suddenly, they felt a strong gust of wind, and heard the sound of small twigs cracking. Leopard went to see where the sound was coming from.

Opening the door, there stood Fire staring at him with red unfriendly eyes. Fire reached out to shake hands with Leopard, but he jumped away and Fire touched his back. With Fire's handprints on him, Leopard ran into the for-est to cool himself.

Seeing that Fire had not come on a friendly visit, poor Leopard's wife jumped out of the window to save herself. Fire went searching through the house until it burned to the ground. Then Fire disappeared in a cloud of blue smoke.

Back in the forest, Leopard sat licking his wounds, for all he had left of his friendship with Fire was the black burned spots where Fire had touched his coat.

He still wears the spots as a reminder of his foolish friendship with Fire.

The King's Goat

(Ivory Coast)

King Boima of Botsumwe had a big, majestic goat. This magnificent animal was the favorite pet of the King. No matter what he did, no one was to touch or chastise the rambunctious goat. King Boima had issued a royal command that anyone accused of molesting the goat would be put to death. No one ever dared to violate the King's command.

Now, in King Boima's kingdom there was a hot-tempered mongoose by the name of Feftah. He had a cassava farm that was his pride and joy. Day after day he would go to the farm and admire his growing plants.

One day Feftah went to his farm, and what should he find? The whole field had been trampled, eaten, and spoiled. Arrogantly standing in the middle of the field was the King's goat, chewing the last cassava plant. Feftah got so vexed that he threw a big stick at the goat. The stubborn goat did not move. Feftah threw a big rock, which struck the goat a mortal blow. In his anger, Feftah had forgotten the King's order: "No person may strike the King's goat on pain of death."

Now that Feftah realized what he had done he began to shake inside his skin. Trying to control himself, he sat down under a cashew nut tree to plan his next move. A nut fell on his head. Plucking the shell from the nut, he ate it. As he sat, more nuts fell. Feftah looked up into the tree and his plan became clear to him.

He picked up the dead goat, carried it up the tree, and hung it head down. Then he went to visit his friend the dog. He showed him the fine cashew nuts and told him where he could get more. Dog gladly went along. Feftah told him, "Shake the tree, good friend, and watch for a bountiful surprise."

With all of his might, Dog shook the tree. And wah! Nuts and the dead goat fell from the tree.

"Oh, ho! Look at what you have done! YOU HAVE KILLED THE KING'S GOAT!" screamed Feftah the mongoose.

"But how?" asked Dog. "I only shook the tree."

"You have to settle with King Boima for killing his goat, and it won't be easy," said Feftah.

"What should I do?" asked Dog.

"Go to him and confess," was Feftah's advice.

Dog picked up the goat and ran home to talk to his wife.

Dog's wife listened to all the details of the nuts, the shaking of the tree, and the dead goat falling down. None of it made any sense to her. Thinking harder, she asked,

"What kind of 'something' is this you are telling me? How can a goat living or dead climb a tree? The mongoose is playing a trick on you. So you must out-trick him. Go by yourself to the King and tell him everything. Then, come back and tell Feftah that the King has no ill feelings about his goat being killed."

Dog did exactly what his wife told him. He carried the goat to King Boima and told him all. When he got back from the King's house, he told Feftah, "King Boima was not vexed. We 'hung heads' for a bit, and then he offered me some of the goat meat. You can see he didn't kill me or even hurt a hair on my head."

Feftah jumped up and down screaming, "That's a mean, low trick. I killed the goat in my cassava patch, and I ought to have my share of the goat's meat."

That was all Dog and his wife wanted to hear. They grabbed Feftah and dragged him to the King. Crying and whining, he begged the King not to kill him. After all, the goat had ruined Feftah's farm. But the King was so angry that he commanded his servants to throw Feftah in the snake pen.

As the soldiers took him to the pen, there was a smile on Feftah's peaked face. His secret power was killing poisonous snakes, so King Boima had done him a favor by putting him in the snake pen. In quick time all the snakes were killed, and Feftah dug an underground path back to his farm.

And so it is that the mongoose still kills any snake that crosses his path. The snake might be carrying the spirit of King Boima's goat.

Which Was the Clever One?

(Ghana)

Old Chief Kesu, the Paramount Chief of Okafora chief-dom, was facing his last days on earth. Ill health, worry, and old age had taken their toll of the old man's strength. He had ruled long and well, and now it was time for him to meet Mr. Death.

Knowing that he would have to choose someone to take his place, Chief Kesu called his three sons to him.

"Issue an order at once that all the village elders, priests, and young men over the age of sixteen gather at the edge of the forest. Then ask the serving boys to bring my three favorite elephants. Now hurry and dress, for there is much to be done this evening."

According to village tradition, one of the Chief's sons would claim the throne, providing he proved himself brave, clever, and wise enough to succeed his father.

When the group had assembled, Chief Kesu addressed them in a weak, quivering voice.

"My good, good friends, as you know, I will be leaving you for a long rest. I have called you here today to help me choose one of my sons as your next chief. I want you to observe carefully, for I shall put each of them to a test.

"Come, my sons, over there under the trees are my three favorite elephants. I want each of you to test your skill against their strength. In whatever manner you handle the animal, you must prove to be its master. Now go good, my sons, and may the cleverest and bravest one of you succeed."

The first son came forward and bowed first to his father and then to the spectators. Laying his spear at his father's feet, he confidently walked over to the waiting elephants. With one snap of his wrist, he pulled the tusks from the bull elephant without drawing a drop of blood.

A loud cheer went up from the crowd at such bravery. "Such a fine deed cannot be outdone by any boy or man," said the village elders.

Now it was the second son's turn. He, too, laid his spear at his father's feet and approached the second elephant. Quicker than a wink, he pulled the heavy gray skin from the animal, all in one piece. With a few folds he draped a robe and presented it to his father.

A great gasp of surprise and admiration, mingled with loud compliments, greeted this extraordinary feat. "Truly no one can surpass such cleverness as that," the young men muttered.

Then the third son's turn came. He came over to his father, knelt down, and kissed both his feet. With soft words he asked his forgiveness for what he was about to do to the last of his favorite elephants.

Walking straight as an arrow, he approached the last elephant. With no effort at all, he lifted the magnificent animal over his head, whirled him around three times, and threw him out of sight.

Every eye followed the giant beast as he sailed through the air. The third son ran under the flying elephant and caught him before he hit the ground. With the grace of a dancer he brought the elephant back in his arms and presented it to his father.

The cheering for the third son was wild, loud, and long. The elders nodded to each other and to the Chief. The young men looked at each other and smiled. Each son had proved himself brave and clever. Each son had also proved something about himself while performing his deed.

Now the elders and the Chief must decide. Which one should they choose? If you were the Chief, which one would you choose?

Bat and the Basket of Darkness

(Ivory Coast)

A long, long time ago when God first made the world, there was never a cold day or a dark night. The sun shone brightly every day, giving light and life to everything on earth. At night, the moon gave a soft blue light that helped man and animals find their way about.

All of this happened when there was no meanness, sorrow, or fear on earth.

One day God called a giant bat to him and said, "Take this kinja [tall covered basket] to the moon. Do not look in it or discuss your journey with anyone. For a long time I have wanted to send a very special 'something' to my friend the moon. He is not properly appreciated by the earth creatures. Go in peace, friend Bat."

The giant bat did not know that the kinja contained a folded patch of darkness. God had not told him, but he did promise Bat that he would later on explain to him his strange gift to the moon.

So, the giant bat put the basket on his back and started on his long journey to the moon. The basket wasn't heavy but the way was very, very long, so Bat put down the kinja to rest. While he was sleeping, the sneaky, curious little monkeys came down out of the trees to see what was in the basket. Thinking there was food inside such a fine-looking basket, one old gray monkey tiptoed up to the basket and opened it. He saw nothing, but the noisy chatter of the monkeys woke up Bat. Before he could clap the lid back on the kinja, the gift of darkness slipped out and quickly scattered among the trees and vines.

In vain, Bat flew about in all directions trying to catch the darkness. As hard as he tried, he wasn't able to catch a single little piece of the gift.

Wearily, he took the empty kinja up to the moon as God had commanded him. When the moon opened the empty basket, she chastised the giant bat for playing a joke on her. Bat tried to explain that the monkeys had opened the basket while he was sleeping and let the gift out.

"Shame on you, Bat, for shirking your duty. God will put a curse on you and all your children. The gift that you were bringing was a patch of darkness that I would use to cool and quiet the world, but since your carelessness caused the gift to escape, you and all your family will fall asleep when the sun shines, and by my weak light you will constantly search for the darkness God sent me as a gift."

As Bat started back to earth the voice of God called out to him, "For your dishonor, you will hide your face in caves and dark corners, because the true, strong light of the sun will blind you."

And so it was with the careless giant bat. At twilight, in all parts of the world, you can still see Bat and his children, and his children's children, flying about in all directions searching for the darkness that escaped from the kinja long, long, years ago.

The Three Prayers

(Ivory Coast)

Owulu, the last son of the poor Masakru family, was over twenty years old and had not taken unto himself a wife. Because he had not been able to gather enough goods, goats, or money for the price of a bride, he was scorned and ridiculed by the village.

Fearing that he would reach old age without a wife of his own, Owulu took his meager belongings and set out to find himself a suitable wife.

In every village he entered he inquired of the Chief if there were any unmarried girls. After it was found out that Owulu did not have the price of a bride, he was quickly sent on his way.

Weary of searching, he stopped at the edge of a small up-country village and asked for food and lodging. After resting for a while, he inquired of the Chief, "Are there any eligible brides who are not spoken for? I am seeking my first wife, but hard times have left me without funds to buy a wife."

69

The Chief hung his head in serious thought. After a moment he said, "Go straight through the town until you come to the last house. The Sakei family lives there. They have an unmarried daughter far past the marrying age. Present yourself to her parents and state your case."

With hope in his heart, Owulu presented himself to the Sakei family. To his great surprise they accepted his marriage proposal without the usual bridal price. As a matter of fact, the parents seemed more than eager for him to marry their last daughter. During all of these deliberations, Owulu hadn't seen the girl he had asked permission to marry. Nor did the parents call her out to meet her future husband.

With much haste, the parents sent word through the village, bidding all their friends to come to the wedding feast.

As the time for the ceremony approached, the girl-bride, covered with many veils, was brought from her hut and led to Owulu's side. The Mullam (Moslem priest) gave the couple his blessings with many long words and bid them "go in peace and go well."

Now that the ceremony was over, the bride, Odienne, made no move to take the veils from her face. Nor did her mother, or any of her female relatives. Such is the usual custom. In his happiness, Owulu did not give such a breach of bridal etiquette a single thought.

Since Owulu had no house for his bride, her father's second wife allowed them to use her house.

When they were alone, Odienne timidly took off her veils, and Owulu had his first look at his bride. Well!, well!, well! *She was the ugliest woman he had ever seen in his life!* Her face was marked with dark patches, ring-worms, and pimples, and her bottom lip hung down too far. Her nose was crooked in two places, and one eye was crossed. Now Owulu understood why the parents were so eager for him to marry their daughter.

Not wishing to offend Odienne, Owulu told her he was going back to his village to tell his family about his marriage and would be gone for seven days.

Owulu had no intention of going to his village, but rather, he wanted to get away and consult a diviner about his marriage problem.

The diviner told him to hang his head and think hard on the three things he wanted most of all and God would answer his prayers. Owulu believed the diviner's words, and returned to his wife with a relieved mind.

He told her of his visit to the diviner and God's promise to answer his three most urgent prayers.

Odienne knew she was ugly and undesirable, so she turned to Owulu and said, "I beg you, husband, please use one of your prayers and ask God to take away my ugliness. I do not want to be a great beauty, but I do want to be acceptable and desirable to my husband."

Just as soon as the sun went behind the trees, Owulu went to his secret place and offered his first prayer. Because he had great faith in God, he ran home and called, "Odienne, Odienne, come to me." And, WAH! approaching him was the most beautiful woman in all the village of Padwah. This was his *wife*. The ugliness had disappeared, and her face was full of happiness. Owulu thought his heart would burst with joy.

Carefully dressing himself in his one good gown, Owulu

proudly took his now beautiful wife walking through the village.

The Chief, sitting in front of his compound, saw the beautiful Odienne and desired her for himself. Without consulting Owulu, he ordered his servants to bring her to him. Not daring to disobey the Chief, Owulu reluctantly let the servants take Odienne to the Chief's compound.

Alone again, Owulu remembered he had not used the other two prayers. So back to his secret place he went to pray. In his frustration and anger, Owulu prayed that his wife be changed into a *monkey!*

Back in the Chief's house, the servants were preparing Odienne for her presentation to the Chief. Suddenly, there was loud screaming by the servants. The beautiful girl had turned into an ugly hairy monkey.

The Chief came to find out what the commotion was all about. There in the middle of the room sat the monkey looking stupidly at the screaming servants.

"But where is the girl Odienne?" asked the Chief. "That girl has been witched," said the Chief's head wife. "She turned herself into a monkey right before our eyes."

"Take that thing out of here," roared the Chief. "No monkey is going to make a fool of me."

The servants took the monkey to Owulu's house and dumped it on the front step.

When Owulu returned from his secret place and saw the monkey, he knew his second prayer had been answered. Knowing he could not live with the shame of having a monkey for a wife, he went back to offer his third and last prayer. With all his might he prayed that his wife would be changed into her old self.

73

The "diviner" gives Owulu three prayers

Returning home again, he found Odienne, as ugly as she had been when they first met. Realizing that life with the ugly Odienne would be a hard thing to live with, Owulu set to work cultivating the ground around their house. With his wife's help, they soon became rich, and Owulu in time forgot Odienne's ugliness.

As years passed she presented him with many fine sons, and Owulu no longer saw the bad features of his wife's face.

For beauty is in the eyes of those who love, and kindness in the hearts of those who share.

Getting What You Deserve

(Ghana)

Eppakah Demba and Lakai Tewar were good and generous husbands who appreciated their wives' beauty. Daily
the wives boasted of their dresses and their jewelry. What
one wife had the other wanted. Constantly, the husbands
were kept searching for ornaments and garments to keep
the wives happy.

Early one morning, Eppakah and Lakai set out in search
of more baubles and bangles. Eppakah stopped at the
riverbank, where there was some beautiful white clay. He
took some of the wet clay and made about twenty-five
small round balls. In the center of each ball he punched a
hole big enough for a string to go through. Then he put
the balls in the sun to dry. Later that afternoon he came
back and painted the beads a bright blue, threaded them
on a strong string, and took them proudly to his wife.

"These are for you, my beautiful one. Wear them well,

for they were made with my own hands," Eppakah told his wife.

"Thank you, husband. There is not another necklace like this one in the whole village. Lakai's wife will burn with envy when she sees this."

Meanwhile Eppakah's friend Lakai had also been searching for some dazzling ornament for his wife. All the morning he had been walking about in the bush, and now he was tired. So he stretched out under a mango tree to rest in the shade.

"Ah-h-h, this is so much better than running up and down in the bush," said Lakai to himself. "That hot sun was making my head hurt."

"Why don't you taste some of my sweet fruit?" asked the mango tree.

"What is this? A talking tree?" asked Lakai.

"Don't let that disturb you. Stranger things have happened. Try one of my delicious plums. You might forget why you are here in the forest," answered the tree.

Lakai threw a stick up the tree and knocked down one of the ripe mango plums. He sat down and bit into the juicy fruit. "Um-mm, this is good. Thank you, tree. Never have I tasted such appetizing fruit. You know, tree, if I had a basket full of these plums I could sell them and get rich."

"Well, well, so you want to become rich? Perhaps I can lead you in the right direction. Look in that hole at the foot of my trunk and you will find all the riches your heart desires."

Lakai scratched the leaves away from the hole and

*Lakai visits the underground home
of Moki the witch*

looked in. His eyes almost popped out of his head at the sight of so many sparkling jewels.

"They are not mine," said the tree. "All of that treasure belongs to Moki, the witch who lives across the way in the cocoa farm. Go and talk to her, but be sure you knock on the ground three times before you speak to her."

"Thank you, tree. I will follow your instructions." Quickly, Lakai crossed over to the cocoa farm and knocked on the ground three times. Instantly Moki came toward him.

"I know what you want, husband-man. Come and visit in my home for a short while. I want to see what kind of man you really are. Promise me you will not laugh at or ridicule anything you see in my house. If you keep this promise, then I will give you what you deserve."

Lakai gave her his promise and followed her into her underground home. It was smoky and foul-smelling, and there were some strange sights, but Lakai kept quiet. There was a hornless goat covered with chicken feathers standing on its head, and a chicken walked around with skin like a snake. The walls were plastered with bones and hair. One table was covered with flowers made out of monkey paws. While Lakai looked around the house, the old witch watched him closely. Lakai neither laughed nor turned up his nose.

When it was time to leave, Moki showed him a huge pot of green bullfrogs who were croaking and jumping all over each other.

Lakai patted the largest frog on the head and said, "Such nice big frogs, Moki."

"I like you, boy," the old witch cackled. "You've got manners and good home training, and I'm going to give you what you deserve. You kept your promise, now I'll keep mine."

Holding Lakai's hand, she led him back to the mango tree and told him to take as many of the jewels as he wanted. He took a large handful and stuffed them in his pocket.

"Thank you, oh, thank you very much, Moki. These will make my wife very happy, and will make me a rich man," said Lakai.

"Go good, my son, and peace be in your home."

Lakai went directly home and called his wife. "Look at the beautiful jewels I have brought you. Wear them with care, for I went through much trouble to get them."

With many sweet words, his wife thanked him for the jewelry. At once she decked herself out with as many necklaces, rings, and bangles as she could. Then she went strolling through the village to show off her new wealth.

The first person she called on was Eppakah's wife. "See all my new bangles my husband just gave me," bragged Lakai's wife.

"Your diamonds are brighter than the sun, while my husband brings me clay beads. Let me find that cheap good-for-nothing."

Seething with anger, she went to find Eppakah. When she found him asleep on his mat, she shook him until his teeth rattled. "How is it that Lakai's wife can wear gold and diamonds while I wear clay beads? If you can't give me better things, then I am going to leave you and go back to my village."

"I know nothing of Lakai's wealth, but I will go and ask him his secret," Eppakah told his wife.

With a heavy heart Eppakah went to his friend and asked him how had he gotten so much jewelry for his wife. "If I don't get some bangles pretty soon, my wife is going to leave me. And you know what shame that would bring me in this village. My manhood would be laughed at."

"For the sake of your marriage I will tell you how I got the jewels," said Lakai as they sat down outside his house.

"First you must go to the big mango tree in the bush. It is a talking tree, so watch your manners. The tree will tell you about the jewels at the foot of its trunk which belong to Moki the witch. Pay attention to what she says to you, and she will give you what you deserve. Now go, and luck go with you."

Eppakah went to the mango tree and sat. The tree said to him, "My fruit is sweet and delicious. Would you like to try some while you are resting?"

"I didn't come here to rest, and I don't want anything to eat. Your fruit doesn't look very appetizing to me. Just tell me where to go, and what to do to get rich," answered Eppakah impatiently.

The tree was shocked by such rude manners, and she rustled her leaves angrily to show her disdain for Eppakah's crudeness. Regaining her composure, she said, "At the foot of my trunk there is a hole filled with rich jewels. They do not belong to me. Moki the witch is the owner, and you will find her over at the cocoa farm.

Maybe she will listen to you, but be sure you knock on the ground three times before you speak to the witch."

Without thanking the tree, Eppakah hurried over to the farm and shouted, "Moki, Moki, you old witch. I want the jewels at the foot of the tree." No one answered his shout. Again he started to shout, "Moki!—" Then it came to him that he was supposed to knock on the ground three times. Grumbling to himself, he stomped on the ground with both feet. "Moki, Moki, hurry up. I haven't much time. My wife is going to leave me if I don't bring her some jewels."

Moki heard Eppakah shouting to her, but his harsh voice had made her feel unkindly disposed toward him. Slowly and doubtfully, Moki opened her door and said to him, "I know why you are here, husband-man. Come into my house and let me see what kind of man you really are. First you must promise me that you will not laugh at anything you see in my house. If you keep this promise, I will give you what you deserve."

"All right, all right, I will promise anything you want, but let's hurry—my wife is waiting for her jewels," replied Eppakah impatiently.

Old Moki shook her head sadly and mumbled some words to herself. Nevertheless, she wanted to give him a chance to prove his true self, so she led him into her strange house. The smoke and the foul odor met Eppakah at the entrance. He held his nose and let out a loud "Whew-w-w!" but when he saw the goat covered with chicken feathers standing on its head, Eppakah burst out laughing. "I say, old witch, this house is quite a sight! And look! A chicken covered with snake skin! For true, Moki,

I have never in my life seen a house as weird as this one. Walls plastered with bones and hair. This place is too much for me. Let us go and get the jewels, old lady."

"Very well, young man. Let us go and get what you deserve," answered Moki as she led the way back to the mango tree. Right away Eppakah began digging in the hole at the foot of the tree.

"Go on and help yourself, for what is in that hole is there especially for YOU," said Moki with a funny smile on her face.

Greedily, Eppakah reached both hands into the hole and pulled out—not gold and diamonds, but huge GREEN FROGS!

"Help! Help! What kind of trick is this, old witch? I came for jewels and you give me frogs. Why? Have you no pity for me? My wife will leave me if I don't bring her the rich jewels she wants. Lakai's wife has diamonds that dazzle the sun. Why do you shame me with these slimy frogs?" asked Eppakah with tears in his voice.

"Young man, for your crude ways and rude manners, you have got what you deserve and more. Each frog you touched will cause a wart to grow on your greedy fingers. The warts will stay with you until you die.

"Now go home and tell your wife to be satisfied with the clay beads. For no home is happy when the wife is envious and jealous of her friends. Your warts will remind you that a man gets what he deserves, and deserves what he gets if his greed exceeds his judgment," said old Moki the witch as she returned to her home.

Krypa, the Troubler

(Ivory Coast)

Facia was an old woman who had seen much grief in her life. Although she had had a large family, all of them had been taken from her by "the one you don't see coming."

When Facia was a child, her mother and father had passed away under what she called "mysterious circumstances." Her uncle and aunt who had reared her to womanhood also died, according to her, in a "peculiar manner."

As Facia approached marriageable age, her pledged husband drowned. A second husband was chosen for her, and all went well for many years. As time passed, she had many children and many grandchildren, but the evil god Krypa was not through with Facia and her family.

One by one her children and her grandchildren were smitten by the dark hand of death, leaving old Facia alone with no one to care for her. Her mind told her it would be a blessed thing to die and be done with the misery and grief of seeing her loved ones taken from her.

Just as Facia was feeling sorry for herself, a strange and unexplainable thing happened. A new burst of life and energy seemed to descend on old Facia. Overnight, she began to look and act younger than her fifty years. Her friends and neighbors whispered behind her back that she was practicing "ju-ju" on herself, or else she had eaten the souls of her dead children.

Facia knew this was not true and set out to prove that her new strength and energy had been given to her for a purpose.

Taking her cooking pot and a cutlass, she journeyed far away from her native village in search of the God who had brought her so much grief and trouble. Facia knew the true God was in heaven, but she also knew that in some manner she must find a way to get up to heaven and talk with him. Perhaps this good God could tell her why Krypa the Troubler had been dogging her footsteps.

Facia cut down trees and made a tall, tall ladder, hoping that it would reach up to heaven, but it wasn't tall enough. With no one to help her, she tried to build a tower to heaven, but her skill at building was not sufficient, so the tower fell down.

Getting a bit discouraged, Facia sat down to rest and to think of another plan. It came to her mind that there ought to be a place where the sky touches the ground. As she looked across the field, this did seem possible. So, surely, there must be a footpath.

With no doubt in her mind, she set out to find the path leading to heaven. As she passed through many different villages, meeting many different tribes, she was the subject of much discussion. Where was such an old woman going alone? What was she searching for?

Facia expected help and sympathy, but no one seemed inclined to sympathize with an old woman who had outlived her family.

One "granny" asked her, "But how do you think you are so different? All people lose their loved ones to Old Man Death. Why do you think he would pass you by?"

These words made Facia realize that the God of Trouble touches everybody, and she would do well to be thankful that he had passed her by thus far.

She never found the path to God's heaven, but she did stop complaining, and lived to the ripe old age of seventy before Krypa sent Old Man Death to call her home.

Monkey's Trick on His Wife

(Ivory Coast)

A long, long time ago when animals married and lived together, there was a monkey and his wife who had a large farm of chickens. His wife loved the chickens so much that she would never cook one for the family. This made monkey-husband so unhappy that he decided to play a joke on his wife. He had wanted some roast chicken for so long that he could taste it, even in his sleep.

Monkey-husband's clever little mind went to work thinking of a sneaky way to get his wife to cook one of her skinny little chickens. When he thought he had his plan perfected, he said to his wife, "I am going across the lake to visit my grandfather. While I am gone Uncle Soni will come and stay with you. Be kind to him for he has only one eye, but he is brave and strong enough to protect you and the chicken farm."

Taking a few things in his wrapping cloth, Monkey pretended to start on his long journey, but he had no intention of going anywhere to visit anybody.

86

He went only as far as the end of his own cassaya patch and built a little hut that could not be seen from the path. Next he took out one of his eyes and wrapped it in a piece of cloth. After folding it carefully, he put it between the branches in a nearby tree so that it would not get bruised or damaged. After all, when his tricky plan was over, he would need both his eyes.

Rearranging his hair and clothes to look like his one-eyed Uncle Soni, Monkey went back to his own house and greeted monkey-wife. She thought it was her husband's uncle, so she welcomed him with refreshments and a bowl of clear soup that had no meat in it. "Uncle Soni" looked at the clear soup and said, "The soup is good, my girl, but it would be better if it had some sweet pieces of chicken in it."

Monkey-wife did not like to have her cooking criticized, so she told him, "My husband loves his chickens so much that he does not want me to kill any of them." Of course, that was not true. It was the wife who did not want to eat any of the chickens. Nevertheless, "Uncle Soni" continued to complain about the thin soup.

"All right," said the wife, "you can have your chicken meat, but I cannot kill the chicken myself. If you do it, I can tell my husband that his uncle killed the chicken, and there will be no palaver."

So "Uncle Soni" killed one of the skinny hens and plucked its feathers off. The wife made more soup, added the chicken, and when it was done, they sat down and ate it all. "Never have I had such a fine meal," said the "uncle," smacking his lips and rubbing his stomach.

After a little more chatter, "Uncle Soni" excused himself, saying he was going for a long walk. When he was out of sight, he ran quickly to his secret hiding place and put his other eye back in his head. Then he sat down and laughed at how he had fooled his wife into thinking he was really his Uncle Soni. Plus the fact he had gotten chicken for dinner.

For four more days Monkey changed his eye, his voice, and his clothes and went back to his wife's house as "Uncle Soni." At each meal he asked for chicken cooked in some special way.

One evening as they were talking and eating, Monkey-wife asked him, "Are you truly my husband's uncle? Sometimes your voice sounds just like his, and you like chicken the way he does. At other times you sound like my husband!"

"Oh, well, girl," said "Uncle Soni." "You know all monkeys talk alike and eat alike, but only Unce Soni has one eye."

Although the wife did not answer, she was not exactly satisfied with "Uncle Soni's" answer. Something about this "uncle" was too familiar.

The next morning she went to the cassava patch to get some greens to cook for herself. She was tired of chicken every day, but most of all, she was unhappy about the decreasing size of her chicken farm.

As monkey-wife was returning along the path with her cassava greens, she saw a small cloth bundle tucked between two branches in the guava tree. Thinking it might be something valuable, she quickly unfolded the cloth, and there staring up at her was the eye of a monkey. "Ah-ha," said the wife to herself, "so somebody is playing a trick. Well, I will also join the trick playing." She ran to her house and got some pepper and rubbed it all over the eye. Then she carefully wrapped it up and put it back in the tree.

Later that day when "Uncle Soni" came for his food, they ate and talked about their distant cousins and the return of her husband, but not one word did she breathe about the eye she had seen in the tree.

Finally, he excused himself, saying that he was going to return to his home since her husband would return in the morning. Thanking her for all the fine food and her good company, "Uncle Soni" bade her good-bye and was off down the path quick as a bird.

With a funny smile on her face, the wife stood in the door and watched him out of sight.

After changing his clothes, "Uncle Soni" took his eye from the tree and put it in the eye socket. "Waah-aaa!" It burned him so badly he had to take it out. Running to the creek, he washed it many, many times and tried it again, but it still burned. Knowing it was time for him to be getting home from his visit, he wet a banana leaf, put the eye back in, and held the leaf over the eye as he ran home.

"How do, wife," said monkey-husband. "Did my uncle take good care of you while I was gone? Did you feed him well?"

Wife knew that she had been tricked into killing her chickens, so she told him, "The trick you played on me was very dirty, but as you can see, you have gotten the worst of it."

She picked up a stick and chased her husband out of the house. To escape her anger, he ran up the nearest tree, and there you will find monkeys today. And you can bet that they do not marry, nor do they like chickens or pepper.

A Father's Blessing to His Daughter

(Ivory Coast)

At the edge of the Gbarbga village, the hunter Dioppo and his wife lived quietly with their two children. The girl-child Maima was beautiful, gentle, and kind, while her brother Jhoko was wild, mean, and selfish. Because the parents were old when Jhoko was born they did not chastise or punish him for his mean ways. His father loved him so much he could not bear for anyone to speak harshly to this wild boy. Consequently, he was disliked and abused by all the village people.

One day as Dioppo returned from a hunting trip, he took to his mat with a high fever. He refused to eat or drink any nourishment. His family knew he was dying. On his last day, the father called his children to him. "In a short time I am going to leave you for good. I have only two things to leave you, my property and my blessing Choose first, my son, while I am able to speak."

Before his father could finish, Jhoko spoke up. "I want your property, Father."

"Then I will take your blessing," replied Maima quietly.

"Kneel down, my child," said the father in a quivering voice, as he put his hands on her head. "The snake will be your friend; guard him well." With these words he turned his head and slipped away in death. Neither Maima nor her mother understood what her father's last words meant, and in their grief they never discussed it again.

The whole village mourned the death of Dioppo, for he had been known for his generosity and bravery. On the fourth day of the funeral feast, the mother suddenly dropped dead. So there was double grief for Maima and Jhoko.

Just as soon as the earth was turned on his mother's grave, Jhoko wanted all of his mother's and father's possessions. The next day he sent six serving boys to Maima's hut to take everything out of her parents' house. Sadly, Maima piled all of the household goods in front of her hut and sat while Jhoko and his servants carried away every grain of rice and every article they could put their hands on. They did not even leave a sleeping mat or cooking pot for his sister Maima. When she rebuked him, he threw one cooking pot down in front of her. "Cook your blessing in that, you stupid duck." With that he walked away laughing, not caring how his sister could get along without food, a sleeping mat, or a weapon to protect herself.

Maima did not complain, but the neighbors saw her need and shared their food with her.

Just before the rainy season, Maima was cleaning the back storeroom and found a large pumpkin seed. Seeing that it was a good seed, she planted it behind her house near the well. With a few words she blessed the seed and the ground that received it, praying that it would bear good fruit.

At the end of a fortnight, Maima was surprised to find the vine full grown with large pumpkins all over the ground. She cut four of the largest ones and carried them to the market. Quickly she sold them. With this small money she bought food for herself and some to share with her neighbors.

Each market day, Maima sold several of her pumpkins, and each time there was a demand for more. The size and sweetness of her pumpkins became well known through-out the countryside. Her wicked brother Jhoko heard about the profit his sister was making from the pump-kins. He became furiously jealous. In his rage he went over to his sister's house and demanded that she give the vine and all the pumpkins to him, because she had used a seed that had belonged to his father.

Maima ran to the vine and gathered the stems in her arms. "Don't harm my plant, for it is all I have." Jhoko drew his cutlass. "Get out of my way. I am going to get rid of that plant once and for all." With one vicious slash he ripped the vines out of Maima's arms. As she tried to grab for them, he slashed madly back and forth across the long tangly vines. With one hard chop he brought the cutlass down with a thud across her wrist. Her right hand fell off. Her screams brought the neighbors, but that didn't stop Jhoko from digging up the roots of the pump-kin plant and throwing them in the well.

The kind neighbors bathed and dressed Maima's wrist and gently carried her to her hut. They nursed her until the stump had healed. When she felt strong enough to walk, she took her small cooking pot and walked into the forest. Fearing that Jhoko might further try to harm her, she hid in the forest trees like an animal. She cried so much and so often that it seemed as if her heart would break.

One day she heard footsteps and voices coming near her. Quickly she ran and hid in the top branches of a tree. Thinking it was her brother, Maima buried her face in her hands and cried so hard her tears flowed to the ground.

One of the men walking under the tree felt the drops of water and thought it was raining. This very special man was Olagah, the son of the district Paramount Chief. Olagah stretched out his hand for the rest of his men to stop. More water fell from the tree on his head. "It is raining! But how is that? It is the middle of the dry season."

One of his servants answered, "It is not raining, Bassa. See, there is not a cloud in the sky."

"But water fell on me," replied Olagah. "Go up the tree and find the source of the falling water."

The servant climbed the tree and found Maima sitting between two limbs crying big crocodile tears. He said nothing to her, but sped down the tree to report his findings to Olagah.

"Bassa, there is a most beautiful girl sitting up in that tree crying like a baby. The water from her eyes fell on you."

Not believing his servant, Olagah climbed up to see for himself. As he looked at her kind face, his heart turned soft inside him. He took her hand. "Come and let me help you down. Then you can tell me why you are up here crying."

When they got to the ground, two of the servants covered her with one of Olagah's fine wrapping cloths and took her to the Paramount Chief's compound.

After the women servants bathed and dressed her, Maima was indeed beautiful, except for the stump of her right hand. She tried to hide it under her blouse, but the servants had already seen it, and silently raised their eyebrows at each other.

When Olagah came in to greet her, she told the whole story of how her brother had mistreated her from the time of her parents' death. As she talked, Olagah's eyes grew misty, and his heart overflowed with tenderness and love for this sad, beautiful girl.

"You must never be afraid again. If you will have me, I would like to take you for my wife," said Olagah. Maima nodded her head in agreement. Olagah went to get his parents to meet his bride-to-be.

Both parents were quite pleased with the grace and charm of the beautiful Maima, but the mother had some misgivings about finding a girl in the forest with one hand cut off. Since the Chief agreed to the wedding, a great feast was prepared and the ceremony took place. There was much rejoicing in the compound, but there were ugly whispers also about the bride. Where did she come from? Why was she in the forest? How had she lost her hand? The Chief heard all these things and turned a deaf ear. The two young people seemed so happy that he could not deny his only son true happiness. So he blessed the marriage and gave them a house to live in and servants to attend their every need.

In due time, Maima presented her husband with a fine boy-child. Again there was rejoicing and feasting throughout the village.

A few days after the feast, Olagah's father asked him to go down to one of the far villages to settle some land palaver. Two large families were disputing the boundary lines of their ancestral property, and the matter needed to be taken care of before it erupted into a tribal war.

Unhappily, Olagah said good-bye to Maima and the baby. He did not fear for their safety while he was gone, because his servants and his father's soldiers were all around the compound.

Meanwhile, across the forest in another village, Jhoko had wasted all his money and lost all his inherited property and was now no more than an unwanted beggar. Having been run out of his town, he decided to try his luck traveling.

He finally arrived in the town where his sister lived, but he did not know this at first. As he listened to the conversations around the village, he heard about the beautiful wife who had only one hand, and whose husband was out of town settling some land palaver for his father. "Ah-ha," said Jhoko to himself. "That must be my sister Maima. She must have enough wealth to give me a splendid gift. Maybe her father-in-law, the great Chief, might give me more if I give him some choice facts about his son's wife."

So Jhoko cleaned himself up carefully and went to the Chief's compound, saying he had some important information for the Chief's ears only.

The Chief listened attentively as Jhoko began his long, rambling tale. "Grand Bassa, your son Olagah is married to a ju-ju woman. She was living in the forest eating nuts and berries when he found her up in a tree. As a child she was a thief, and her hand was cut off to shame her. Because she witched so many men with her tricky ways, the village elders drove her from their town. Not only did she put evil spells on her many husbands, but she killed them to satisfy her ku [agreement] with the forest spirits. I have come to warn you to get rid of this woman before she harms your son and grandson. Act quickly before Olagah gets back." The Chief's first thought was to kill Maima at once, but he could not bear to kill his only grandson. So he ordered his soldiers to take the two of them deep into the forest and leave them there.

As soon as Maima and the child were taken away, her wicked, lying brother Jhoko went back to the Chief to receive his reward for the choice information. The Chief and his wife thanked him with the gift of a small house near their compound, and a small bag of coins.

Back in the forest, Maima was trying to figure out why her father-in-law had ordered her out of her husband's house. Had she done something to offend him? Had her husband banished her to the forest because he did not want her any longer? No one had explained anything to her. The soldiers only told her, "If you return, you and your son will be killed immediately."

After feeding the baby, Maima rested in the tall grass. Suddenly, she heard a swishing sound. Quickly covering the baby with her body, she saw a green cassava snake headed straight toward her. Before she could scream, the snake said, "Help me, good woman, my life is in danger." Realiz-ing that the snake was talking, Maima said, "Crawl into

96

my pot and lie quietly." Just as she put the lid on the pan, another snake came up to her. He raised his head as if to strike. "Have you seen one of my kind pass this way?"

"Oh, yes," replied Maima. "He went behind that far tree just a minute ago."

"Thank you," said the enemy snake as he hastened through the grass.

"Can I come out now?" asked the snake in the pot. Maima turned the pot down and the friendly snake crawled out and continued to talk to her.

"Don't be afraid of me. I will not hurt you or your child. Tell me, good woman, why are you way out here in the forest alone?"

"My husband's father drove me out of my house while my husband was away and asked me not to return. I do not know why I have been treated this way. Will you help me? I have nowhere to go."

"Come with me," said the snake. "You helped me once, so I will do what I can for you and the child."

As Maima put the baby on her back, she felt a warm glow in the stump of her right hand. When she looked down, there was her right hand with all its fingers right where they should be. It was healed and attached to her wrist. For a moment her heart stopped beating. Her joy at having her hand back made her shout out loud, "I have both my hands, I have both my hands."

"That is only a part of the blessing that will come to you," answered the snake, as he crawled through the grass.

At last they came to the Kingdom of the Snakes. Maima was given a great welcome by all the snakes, as they thanked her for saving the life of one of their members.

After spending many pleasant days with the snakes, Maima told her friends that it was time for her to try her luck again in the Land of Men. Her baby needed to know and be with those of his own kind. The snakes understood and gathered good-bye gifts for her.

Her close friend, the green cassava snake, gave her a ring made of twisted strands of gold. He told her to wear it always to keep her body from harm. The chief snake gave her a small black box with these instructions: "Keep the box near you night and day. When you want anything, just open the box and repeat your wish. Everything you desire will come true for you, but be sure no one opens the box except you or your child."

Maima thanked the snakes and made her way back to her village.

When she arrived at the edge of town, she opened the little black box and made a wish for a house. In an instant there appeared a most beautiful house complete with servants, cattle, garden plots, and full storehouses. With so much wealth, Maima settled down to the life of a rich lady.

Meanwhile, Olagah had returned from his trip. His father told him that his wife and son were dead, and showed him the false graves to prove it. Poor Olagah grieved so hard that his father thought he was losing his mind. Many times his father was tempted to tell Olagah the truth, but his wife held him back.

"It is better to leave it so," she said. "Let him believe

that she is dead. She might have witched him and the child. There is a rich lady living in a new house at the edge of the village. Let us take him to meet her. Perhaps it will help him to forget the lost Maima."

The next day Olagah went with his parents to the house of the rich lady. To their surprise there was Maima coming down the path holding her baby in her arms. Olagah ran toward her crying, "Is it really you, Maima? My father told me that you and the child were dead. What kind of joke is this, father?" asked Olagah.

"Forgive me, my son, but a certain man came to my house and told me that Maima was a witch. We were so afraid that she might put a spell on you, that we sent her away."

"My mind tells me that the certain man who told you those falsehoods was my wicked brother Jhoko. He would stop at nothing to get money. He was the one who cut off my hand," said Maima.

The Chief ordered his soldiers to find the evil Jhoko and kill him on sight. But Maima begged him to spare Jhoko's life. Nevertheless, Jhoko was stripped of all his ill-gotten possessions and driven into the bush with not one piece of clothing on his body. The animals would give him his just due.

Maima also asked the Chief to issue a command that no snakes be killed in their village, because their friendship had healed her hand and brought her safely back to her loved ones.

And so it was that the blessing of her father was fulfilled, and Maima and Olagah lived to a happy old age together.

The Greatness of Man

(Ivory Coast)

Long, long years ago when animals talked to each other, the leopard thought he was the greatest and most power-ful creature on the face of the earth. Through his strength and prowess, Leopard appointed himself King of the Jungle.

One day as he prowled through his kingdom, he met a skinny chicken who was cackling and running as if the devil was after her.

"Ho, there, little one, why are you running so fast? Has something frightened you?"

"Don't stop me, King Leopard. I am running away from Man," answered the chicken.

"Hold on there a minute, my feathered subject. Did I understand you to say that you are running away from Man? What kind of creature is he?"

"Well," said Chicken as she paused to catch her breath, "Man stands upright on two hairy legs, and his head looks down on everything. His long arms swing back and forth as he walks. He keeps you near his house, feeds you, and then, when he is hungry, he eats you. With his boom-boom in his right hand he claims to be the cleverest crea-ture on earth."

"Now, now, little one, you know that is not true. Every animal in the forest knows that I am the most powerful and the most respected creature God has made, and no two-legged animal can excel me," boasted King Leopard.

"Say what you wish," said the hen, "but I am going to stay clear of Man, because I want to live. Good-bye, Great One, and take care." Off flew the chicken to the nearest tree to hide.

King Leopard sat down to think on the chicken's words. As he sat chewing and thinking, a bush ox came hurrying through the tall grass.

"Why are you in such a hurry, my good friend? The day is much too hot for games. Sit down and cool your-self."

The bush ox regarded the invitation as a command and immediately sat a respectful distance from the king. "Oh, sir," said the ox, "I have had a hard time serving Man. He has made me pull his loads, plow his fields, grind his grain, and then, when I am old, he kills me. So you see, I must get as far away from Man as I can."

"That sounds like the same creature Chicken told me about. Stay here with me and Man will not bother you," offered King Leopard.

"No thank you, sir," replied the ox. "I am going to find a hiding place far away from here where Man cannot find me." And away lumbered the ox through the tall bush.

Before the bush ox was out of sight, a gray horse covered with sweat came galloping up the path. He stopped
suddenly when he saw King Leopard.

"Stand still for a minute and tell me why you are in
such a hurry. It is much too hot for racing games today,"
said King Leopard.

"I must tell you, Royal One, I am running away from
the horrible creature called Man. He has misused and
abused me. I have been beaten, and raced until my legs
were numb. Many times my back has been loaded with
boxes, bags, and parcels weighing hundreds of pounds.
I must work when the sun is hot, and when the rains come
down. Then, when I am too old to be sold or traded, I am
taken to the bush and shot. Oh, yes, I am running away
from Man, and you would do well to follow me." And
off he went to find a hiding place.

King Leopard sat still and thought on the things the
animals had told him. The cool shade of the tree made
him sleepy. As Leopard dozed, a long, tall shadow fell
across him. "Oh, ho, and who is this?" asked the sleepy
king.

"I am Man," answered the tall creature. "And you
must be the powerful King of the Jungle. For one as great
and powerful as you, your home in this bed of grass does
not do you honor."

"It is the best my subjects could offer me. Do not criti-
cize if you cannot help. After all, I have many homes
throughout my kingdom."

"Then," said Man, "I will build you another house
different from any you have seen." So Man built a house
shaped like a cage. "Now, here is a house fit for royalty.

Enter, King Leopard, and see if you approve of my ef-
forts."

Just as soon as Leopard walked into the cage, Man
closed the door and bolted it.

"But what is this?" asked Leopard. "How dare you
embarrass me in this ridiculous fashion? Open this door
immediately." Man ignored Leopard's pleading, and called
four other men, who took the cage and put it on a boat
that sailed away to the Land of Man.

Leopard learned the hard way that when Man comes
to the jungle, all animals should run, for there is no creature who can excel the cunning and craftiness of Man and
his sons.

The Bowl of Fu-Fu

(Ivory Coast)

Allu Kofi was known for his lazy ways and enormous appetite. Day in and day out his wife nagged him to stop sleeping all day in the hammock and get busy with the farm chores. The time for planting was almost over, and Allu had done nothing to stop his wife Moya's nagging. Each day he told her, "Wait small, the planting will get done and the crops will be gathered. Just don't humbug me so much."

At long last, Allu got tired of Moya's nagging, so he took his farm tools and a bowl of food and went to the farm to start planting a patch of ground peas (peanuts).

When Allu arrived at the farming site, he looked it over, and thought perhaps it might be better if he sat under a tree and planned what to do first. While sitting and thinking, Allu absent-mindedly started eating the ground peas that he was supposed to plant. The more he thought about all the work that had to be done out in the hot sun, the faster the ground peas disappeared in Allu's mouth. Soon there were no peas left in the basket, and Allu immediately fell asleep.

Allu woke up just as the sun was going down. Nothing had been done in the field and all the ground peas were gone. Not wanting to face his wife's anger, Allu smeared dirt on his hands, clothes, and his hoe. Pretending to be very tired, he walked wearily home.

Moya was so happy to see her husband dirty and tired from his day at the farm that she fixed him a hot bath and a fine meal of his favorite foods. As he ate, he told her of the "hard work" digging and planting the ground peas. This routine went on for quite some time. Little did Moya know about the big joke that Allu was playing on her every day he left the house. She thought he was working, but all that lazy Allu did was to go down to the farm, find a big shady tree, and sleep. Each evening he dirtied his clothes and told her how well the crop was doing.

Finally, the time arrived for the peas to be harvested. Moya wanted to go with Allu and help, but he said, "Oh, no, no, no, that kind of work is too hard for you. When the sun goes down, I will go and gather the ground peas." Moya was flattered by such strange words coming from a man as lazy as Allu. But she said nothing.

Allu knew he would have to bring ground peas home, or else there would be no peace. So he went to his neighbor's farm and took four baskets of peas and ran home with them. That night there was rejoicing in the Kofi household. Pea soup for evening "chop." How wonderful!

Three days later, Allu took seven baskets of nuts from his neighbor's farm. By this time, his neighbor was suspicious and wondered if animals or humans were stealing his ground peas. He discussed the loss with his wife, who decided to make a bowl of thick fu-fu and put it near the last stack of drying peanuts. Into the mixture she put three large pods of red pepper. That would give the thief a burned-up throat, if he was greedy enough to stop and eat.

The next visit Allu made to his neighbor's field, he saw the big bowl of fu-fu, and he couldn't believe his eyes. Right away he forgot all about the ground peas and grabbed a handful of fu-fu and crammed it into his mouth. The thick peppery mixture stuck in his mouth, and he couldn't swallow it. He tried to scream, but his throat had closed up. As he jumped up and down in pain, he accidentally jumped into the bowl and flopped down in the hot sticky goo. The fu-fu was like a vise, and it was all over him.

The hot pepper was burning his mouth, face, feet, and hands. His feet were heavy with the fu-fu and the bowl stuck to them. So there was nothing to do but wait until daylight.

Early the next morning, the neighbor came to check on the bowl of fu-fu. Lo and behold! Here was his neighbor Allu Kofi, sitting in the bowl looking like a giant spider caught in a web. A web of fu-fu!

The neighbor called the villagers to come and see what his bowl of fu-fu had caught. When Allu's wife saw her husband sitting in the bowl of fu-fu, she knew he had lied to her about his work on the farm. Feeling shame and anger, Moya ran quickly and got hot water to thin the fu-fu.

Just as soon as Allu was able to free his feet, he started running as fast as he could away from the field. Right behind him was his neighbor with a big stick.

Allu was driven out of the village of Bakarada, and no one has seen or heard from him since.

The neighbor took Allu's wife into his household as his second wife. For many years they lived and worked happily together, never mentioning the strange catch that was found in the bowl of fu-fu.

Too Much Loyalty

(Ghana)

Many, many years ago in the village of Ambari, two women who were dear, close friends gave birth to girl-children on the same day, at the same hour, in the same month. The first friend named her daughter Titi, and the second friend named her daughter Yele.

As the girls grew, they became inseparable. Some of the villagers said that the girls were so close that they walked, talked, and acted alike. While they were still young, Titi and Yele took a secret oath to remain friends and inseparable for life. To seal their oath, they pricked their forefingers, and held them together so that their blood would mix and mingle as they pledged their loyalty to each other.

At the age of twelve they were initiated into the secret rites of womanhood. And now came their moment of truth. Titi's father chose a husband for her and arranged the dowry and wedding without consulting Titi or her mother. It was his prerogative to secure a suitable husband for his eligible daughter as soon as possible. He did not want a thirteen-year-old unmarried daughter on his hands.

Sadly, Yele watched her friend's wedding. Her parents were not able to gather a sufficient dowry to secure a husband for her, or to bargain with Titi's husband for Yele to become his second wife. All through the long marriage ceremony, Yele's eyes were filled with tears. Her good, good friend would be leaving her behind, and the thought of so much loneliness brought more tears.

At last the ceremony was over, and it was time for Titi to gather her things and follow her husband to his village. Seeing the tears in Yele's eyes, Titi began crying also. "Wait here, Yele. I will ask husband Ayo if you can come with us. He cannot refuse me this one favor."

Quickly she ran to her new husband. "Ayo, may my friend Yele come with us to your village? She is like a sister to me, and it would break my heart to leave her. I beg you, Ayo, please let her come. She will be no trouble."

Ayo listened impatiently to Titi. He was anxious to get started for his village. "No, no, no, Titi. I have taken only one wife, and I want no part of your friend at this time. A man has the right to be alone with his new wife. Now go and pick up your things. It is time for us to go."

Titi ran to her mother and asked her to beg Ayo to take Yele with them. "My child, you should not press your new husband too much. You hardly know him. Wait here and I will ask him."

With some grumbling, Ayo agreed that Yele could come with them as Titi's serving girl.

With this matter settled, all three journeyed to Ayo's village. When they arrived, he told Yele she could not share the house with them, because the house had been prepared especially for the wedding couple.

Titi sat down outside the house and pouted, saying, "If Yele can't come in, then I won't either." This made Ayo so vexed that he shook with anger. "What kind of marriage is this? Are you a baby or a woman? Have you forgotten that you are my wife, and Yele is supposed to be your serving girl? She can stay over at my mother's house. Now, bring your things on into the house and make me some supper."

"But, Ayo, Yele is my friend, not my servant. We made a pledge when we were children that we would never be separated. Don't let your anger shame our friendship. Yele loves you just as I do," replied Titi.

Too tired and too frustrated to argue any more, he yielded to Titi's wishes. So, day after day, night after night, Titi, Yele, and Ayo slept and ate together with constant grumbling from Ayo.

After two weeks of this uncomfortable arrangement, Ayo was ready to do anything to get rid of the ever-present Yele. With a heavy heart he went to the village Chief and discussed his problem. He loved his young wife very much, but he had had enough of his wife's friend Yele. The Chief told him, "I have one solution to this marriage palaver. Soon it will be time for the Yam Festival, at which time we will sacrifice three unmarried girls to the Harvest God. Get your wife's friend to attend the festival, and we will see that she is one of the girls chosen for the blood sacrifice. Now, go, and free your mind of the troublesome Yele."

Three weeks later the time was right for the festival. The crop of yams this year had been exceptionally large. Consequently there was much joy throughout the village. Yet in some houses there was fear that their unmarried daughters might be chosen for the annual sacrifice.

Not knowing what was before them, Titi and Yele dressed in their finest lapas and joined Ayo on the path to the festival. As they reached the clearing at the edge of the yam field, the smell of food cooking and smoke greeted them. The whole village was celebrating with feasting, dancing, and singing.

When the drums and the dancing grew to a hysterical pitch, the girls to be sacrificed were suddenly pulled from the crowd by three masked and costumed figures. Scream-ing and crying, the girls were taken to the altar of the Harvest God. Of course, Yele was one of the girls selected. Titi screamed, "No, no, no-o, not Yele. She does not be-long to your village." She tried to follow her friend, but the crowd held her back.

Yele was gone for good. In a short while her blood and that of the other two girls would mingle with the soil of the bountiful yam field.

Joyfully Ayo led the grieving Titi home. She went in-side, picked up her mat, took it a short distance from the house, and sat down. She refused to eat or speak. Both day and night she sat staring at the ground. Her grief was so great that it was a pitiful sight to see.

At last, one day, she stretched out on her mat. Death came and took her to join her friend Yele.

Ayo grieved loud and long for his young wife, but the neighbors did not sympathize with him. They blamed him for all the sadness. For it was he who had asked the Chief to get rid of Yele, and it was he who had caused Titi's grief and her death.

For his selfish wish to separate the two childhood friends, his friends and neighbors shunned and scorned him for the remainder of his life.

Alone and friendless, he left the village and wandered in the forest until his end came.

Titi's loyalty to her friend had brought Yele to this strange village and a strange death. And in the end, her loyalty caused her own death. Which proves that too much loyalty is just as bad as not enough. But the two friends were reunited in death for ever and ever and ever.

A Good Deed Is Strangely Repaid

(Ivory Coast)

A long, long time ago when animals could talk and think like human beings, there lived a huge crocodile in the Comoe River. This adventurous old crocodile was forever on the lookout for new and different kinds of food to satisfy his enormous appetite. One evening he ventured out of the river in search of something different. As night came on he got lost and could not find his way back to the river. So he spent the night hiding under a pile of old trees.

Early in the morning Mr. Crocodile began to feel the uncomfortable rays of the sun on his back. He knew if he did not get back to the river soon he would die of thirst and sunburn. The old tree stumps provided a little shade, but no water. His loud panting frightened Gadalo, a small boy who had come to the forest to get wood for the family's morning fire.

"What are you doing here, Mr. Crocodile? You are

114

mighty far from the river, aren't you?" asked Gadalo.

"Don't stand there asking stupid questions. You can see that I am lost. Take me to the river before I die in this awful sun," replied the impatient crocodile.

"Wait a moment while I carry this wood to my house. Then I will help you."

Quickly he ran home and left the wood. Thinking of a way to carry the crocodile, he picked up a straw mat and a strong piece of rope. Gadalo was only ten years old, but he was strong for his age.

When he returned to Mr. Crocodile, he told him, "All right now, old one, roll over on this mat and I will tie you up so that the sun can't reach you." With one big heave, Gadalo put the mat with heavy Mr. "Croc" rolled up in it on his head and walked toward the river.

Just as soon as he got to the riverbank, he untied the mat and let the crocodile out.

"Oh, please don't put me down here. My skin is so scorched that my legs are stiff. Do carry me into the water," pleaded Mr. Crocodile.

Lifting the heavy crocodile in his arms, Gadalo walked into the water up to his knees. Then he started to put the croc down.

"Please, please, I beg you, don't put me down here. The water is too shallow. Go a little farther out, until the water comes up to your stomach."

"Mr. Crocodile, you are a hard one to please, but I'm trying. I didn't know you wanted so much service."

Gadalo continued on into the water until it reached his stomach. Again he attempted to put the crocodile down.

"Not yet, my little one. Wade on a bit more, until the

115

water reaches the roundness of your shoulders. Then I am sure the water will be deep enough for me to swim."

On went Gadalo into the deep water. When it swirled around his shoulders, Mr. Crocodile nudged him. "Now put me down. This is my special place in the river."

Gadalo put him gently down in the water and started to walk back out.

"Just a minute, little one. I must reward you for your service." With a big splashing of his tail, the crocodile knocked Gadalo down and grabbed his leg tightly.

"What is the matter with you, Mr. Crocodile? Let go of my leg. You are hurting me."

"Let you go? No, no, my little friend. I have not eaten a good meal for a whole day, and I'm not going to let you get away. Your two legs will not make a good mouthful, but they will help to ease my hunger while I anticipate the rest of your skinny body."

"Oh, Mr. Crocodile, you wouldn't eat me, would you? Didn't I do you a good turn by bringing you here? Is this how you will repay my kindness to you?" asked Gadalo.

"You stupid, stupid boy. Don't you know that good deeds are always rewarded by evil ones?" cackled the haughty crocodile.

"But that is not true, Mr. Crocodile. You are just making that up to prove that you are justified in eating me. Nobody in this whole wide world will agree with you. My mother taught me that kindness is always repaid in kindness."

"Fie on your mother," snapped the angry reptile. "Within an hour I can find three people who will agree with me. Just watch and see."

116

No sooner had he finished boasting, when along came an old woman to wash her clothes in the river.

"Good day, old woman," said the crocodile. "Before you begin your work, will you answer a question for me? Do you think a good deed should be rewarded with kindness or with wickedness?"

"Ai-yah, Mr. Crocodile, I am old, and I know that the good deeds are repaid in sorry, selfish deeds. Let me tell you why I say that. When I was young, I worked hard for my husband. Year after year I gave him many children, tended his farm, cooked his food, carried his loads on my head, and suffered his abuse. Now that I am old, I have been put aside to die in the bush, while a young wife takes my place. Oh, yes, I know for true that good is rewarded with evil," replied the old woman.

"See, little Gadalo, what did I tell you? The first person I asked agreed with me," announced Mr. Crocodile joyfully.

"But that was only one old lady, and she doesn't know everything," replied Gadalo.

The old woman went about her business of washing her few faded clothes. Mr. Crocodile and Gadalo waited in the water for someone else to come to the river. In a short while a warrior came limping down to the river to wash the blood from his leg.

As the warrior bent down to get a handful of water, Crocodile interrupted him. "I say there, good friend, will you settle an argument for us? I told this boy that a good deed should be rewarded with an evil one, but he says that a good deed should be rewarded with kindness. Which one of us would you agree with?"

117

"Wait a moment while I put some cold water on my wound. The pain is running all over my body. Now, as to your question, let me tell you what happened to me and maybe you can judge for yourself. I was on my way home from the city, when I saw a bush dog caught in a trap. Seeing that he was in great pain, I opened the trap and let him loose. He repaid my kindness by savagely biting my leg. As you can see, he almost tore my leg off."

"Ah-ha," rejoiced Mr. Croc, "then you will agree whole-heartedly that your good deed was rewarded intentionally with an evil deed?"

"Indeed I do," replied the warrior. "That dog begged me with his sad eyes to help him, and for my trouble, he almost did me in."

Turning to Gadalo, Mr. Crocodile asked him, "Now do you believe me? Two fine people have agreed with me. I am trying to be patient with you, but my hunger is growing great. You will have exactly one more chance, and then you will be my first meal for the day."

"I don't care what you say, Mr. Crocodile, I don't believe everybody in the world believes as you do. Eating me will not prove anything other than that you are a selfish, greedy, evil thing who repaid kindness with unkindness."

"Think your own thoughts and I'll think mine, and in the end we will know who was right," replied Mr. Crocodile with confidence.

As he was gloating over his small victory, a chief and two servants came down to the river to bathe.

With enthusiasm the old crocodile greeted him. "Good

day, Honorable Chief. In your great wisdom, would you do me the honor of answering an important question for me? Is it not true that a good deed is rewarded with an evil one?"

"Before I answer your question, you must tell me why you are holding the boy," answered the wise Chief.

"Well, you see, Chief, it was like this. I wandered out of the river late one evening and got lost in the bush. This boy found me and brought me back here, and since I have not eaten all day, I intend to make a meal of him. It would be stupid of me to let him go, because if I don't get food, I will die. Do you understand, great Chief? If I don't eat him, I would have to go and look for food," whined the selfish crocodile.

"Wait a minute, Crocodile, do you want me to believe that this small boy brought you all the way from the bush to this river?" asked the chief.

"For true, Chief, I carried him all by myself. He would have died if I had left him out there in the sun," replied Gadalo.

"I won't believe it unless you show me how it was done. Come up out of the water, you two, and let's get to the bottom of this matter." Gadalo and the crocodile came up on the riverbank in front of the Chief.

"Now, young man, show me how you handled this heavy load."

"Well," said Gadalo, "I took the straw mat and stretched it out on the ground. Then I told Mr. Crocodile to roll over on the mat. When the crocodile was all the way on the mat I rolled the mat up."

119

"That's the first thing you did, huh? All right, Croco-dile, lie down on the mat, and let me see if the boy is telling the truth," instructed the Chief.

Without asking a question, Mr. Crocodile stretched out on the mat, and Gadalo rolled him up.

"Now what else did you do?" asked the Chief.

"I tied him up with this rope," answered Gadalo.

"Show me how you tied up the mat."

With nimble fingers, Gadalo tightly looped the rope around the mat and tied the knots securely.

"After you tied the mat up, what did you do then?"

"I put the mat with Mr. Crocodile in it on my head and brought it here," answered Gadalo.

"Well, well," said the Chief, "since you have the croco-dile all nicely tied up, why don't you take him home and make a nice meal of *him*. Eat hearty, and don't forget that kind deeds have strange ways of being rewarded."

Gadalo shows the Chief how he wrapped up Mr. Crocodile

Obey Your Parents

(Ghana)

Once upon a time in the land of the Akan people, there lived a man and his three sons. Knowing that his life was coming to an end, the father called the boys to him for a few last words of advice.

As the boys sat around their dying father, he told them, "In a short time I will be leaving you for good. I want you to bury my body next to your mother's grave. Because it is the custom in our family, I want all three of you to watch over my grave for seven days. On the seventh day, when you have finished your watching, you will come face to face with a strange 'something' on the homeward path. Do not run or be afraid of it. No harm will come to you if you promise to keep watch over my grave." Each brother gave his promise.

Just before dawn of the next day, their father died quietly in his sleep. Promptly the boys sewed him up in his burial cloth and put him in the grave beside his wife.

On that same day there was a dance competition held in a nearby village. In that village were three beautiful sisters, who announced that they would marry the winners of the dance contest.

The two older brothers decided to try their luck in winning one of the beautiful girls for a wife. The youngest son shook his head in disbelief. "You have forgotten Papa's last words. He told us to bury him and watch over his grave for seven days, and on the seventh day to come back to the house. Ai-yah! My brothers, surely you are not going to dance before Papa's body is cold? Don't forget you gave your word to a dying man."

"Stop talking foolishness. What easier way could we get rich young wives, than to win the dance contest? We are already the best dancers here in our village and it will be easy for us to win. After all, we must look to better ourselves," argued the older brothers.

"Go on and try to win your wives, but I will keep watch as Papa asked us to do. It is not a good thing to break a promise made to the dead," replied the youngest brother.

All the morning, the older boys bathed themselves down at the river. In the afternoon, they dressed in their finest robes and left to join the other dancers in the contest. As the dancers pranced around the circle showing off their fanciest steps, a tall young man dressed in a leopard skin appeared at the edge of the dance field. As the handsome young man strutted around the circle throwing gold coins to the people, the dancers stopped to watch him. When he came face to face with the three sisters, he looked lovingly at the oldest girl and handed her his bag of gold coins. With a few soft words of love she followed him as he walked away from the crowd. He led her to a new house that was too beautiful for words. He opened the door, ushered her in, locked the door, and went on his way.

Having seen one sister taken by the stranger, the brothers returned home dejected. Immediately they went to find their younger brother. He was still sitting at the grave keeping watch.

"Young one, we must tell you what happened at the competition. A fine-looking stranger dressed in a leopard skin enticed one of the sisters away with his generous gifts of gold and sweet talk. The competition was called off after she followed him away," reported the older boys.

On the following day the competition began again, and again the older brothers went back to try their luck, while the young one continued to watch at the grave.

The dance contest was in full swing when the stranger appeared again at the edge of the dance field. This time he was dressed in fine gold amulets and white country cloth. He was indeed a handsome sight to behold. Again he threw gold coins to the dancers and scattered coins among the people crowded around the field. He caught the eye of the second beautiful sister. She sweetly smiled and followed him as he beckoned to her. Like the first sister, he led her to a beautiful house far in the bush, locked her in, and went on his way.

More dejected than ever, the older boys returned home to find their brother still keeping his watch at the grave. They told him about the second appearance of the rich, handsome stranger, and how he had dazzled the second sister with his wealth and good looks.

As the brothers described the events of the evening, the young brother said nothing, but there was a half smile and a twinkle in his eye.

Now there was only one sister left, and only one more day of competition. This was the brothers' last chance. So, early in the morning, they went down to the river and thoroughly bathed themselves all over. Then they carefully groomed their hair, put on their best robes, and painted some intricate designs on their faces. They hoped that their beauty would attract the eye of the last sister.

When they arrived at the village, the dancing had started, but they joined the group and performed the steps to perfection. As the people clapped and sang their praise, the stranger casually strolled onto the dance field. Again, he threw money to the dancers and to the audience.

The third sister was so impressed with his wealth that he had no trouble leading her away from the crowd. She, too, was ushered into a beautiful new house and locked in.

The competition was over. The brothers had won no wives. Sadly they returned to their brother. "We have acted very selfishly, young one. Now that we have no wives, we will watch with you."

"It's too late for you to start now. For three days you have ignored Papa's wish, and you know the penalty for disobedience. The dead never forget a broken promise." So, alone, the younger brother stayed at the grave until the seven days were up.

On the seventh day, as the sun was going down, the grave opened up and out stepped their father.

"My son, where are your brothers? Couldn't they wait seven short days?"

"They were trying to get wives, Papa."

"Never mind, my son. Return to the house. Your reward is waiting for you." With these words the grave opened and his father disappeared.

As the boy put his foot on the homeward path, a giant monkey blocked the way. "Follow me," the monkey said. Without any fear, the young one followed the giant black monkey far into the bush. With one swish of his hairy hand, the animal knocked down three large cottonwood trees. In an instant, the trees turned into three beautiful houses, and in each house was one of the three beautiful sisters.

"All of this is yours," said the monkey. "I am the spirit of your dead father. For your loyal and obedient ways, you will have much wealth and happiness all your days. As for your brothers, they will continue to wander about from village to village seeking wives. Old age will find them alone and childless, until death brings them face to face with their father."

And thus it was that obedience and loyalty had their just reward.

About the Author

Edythe Rance Haskett is a teacher from Norfolk, Virginia. She has studied at Shaw University in Raleigh, N.C., where she earned her A.B., and at New York University, where she received her M.A. Mrs. Haskett studied further at Rutgers University and at the Institute of African Studies, Columbia University.

Mrs. Haskett has made three trips to West Africa, at one time staying for two years to teach in Liberia. During her travels up and down the west coast of Africa she collected the tales told in this book.